Mousse•Pudding
慕思•布丁

62>> Taro Mousse Trifle 芋頭慕思	78>> Milk Tea Coffee Pudding 鴛鴦奶茶咖啡布丁
64>> Lavender Mousse Cake 薰衣草慕思蛋糕	80>> Coconut Pudding 椰纖果果凍
66>> Durian Panna Cotta 榴槤奶酪	82>> Water Chestnut Agar-agar with Yam 山藥馬蹄果凍
68>> Red Bean Mousse Cake 紅豆慕思蛋糕	84>> Durian Mousse 榴槤芝士慕思
70>> Beancurd Mousse 豆腐慕思蛋糕	86>> Black Glutinous Rice Pudding 香蕉紫米布丁
72>> Cappuccino Mousse 卡布基諾慕思	88>> Sesame Peanut Pudding 芝麻花生布丁
74>> Sour Sop Mousse 紅毛榴槤慕思	90>> Yogurt Pudding 乳酪布丁
76>> Caramel Coffee Mousse 焦糖咖啡慕思	92>> Longan Sorbet 龍眼冰沙

Cheesecake
芝士蛋糕

96>> Lemon Cheesecake
檸檬芝士蛋糕

98>> Tiramisu
意大利芝士蛋糕

100>> Herb and Cheese Scone
香料芝士鬆餅

102>> Low Fat Cheesecake
低脂乳酪芝士蛋糕

104>> Light Cinnamon Cheesecake
輕軟肉桂芝士蛋糕

106>> Chocolate Mint Cheesecake
薄荷芝士蛋糕

108>> Supreme Chocolate Cheesecake
朱古力芝士蛋糕

110>> Raspberry Cheese Roll
覆盆子芝士卷

Pie•Tart•Puff
派•塔•泡芙

114>> Linzer Torte 林芝塔	126>> Pine Nut Tarts 松子塔
116>> Pumpkin Tarts 南瓜塔	128>> Durian Chocolate Puffs 榴槤朱古力泡芙
118>> Almond Fruit Tarts 水果杏仁塔	130>> German Cheese Tarts 德國芝士塔
121>> Napoleon 拿破崙派	133>> Apple Strudel 蘋果酥餅
124>> Mango Pie 芒果派	

Tea•Coffee
茶•咖啡

138>> Cinnamon Apple Tea
蘋果肉桂茶

140>> Jasmine Iced Coffee
茉莉茶冰咖啡

141>> Rose and Rosemary Tea
玫瑰迷迭香茶

142>> Lemongrass Mint Tea
薄荷香茅提神茶

About Egg White

關於蛋白

Egg white has an indispensable role in baking and pastry world. Egg white traps air after being beaten and it allows the batter or dough mixture to expand into wonderful forms in the baking process. Egg white in souffles brings a light and fluffy texture while egg white in mousse makes it silky smooth.

In the cookbook, various stages of beaten egg white are mention, namely "foamy," "soft peaks" and "stiff".

Foamy: When the egg white is lightly beaten, it starts to turn white with large bubbles in it. Yet, such bubbles break easily if the egg white is not beaten continuously.(as shown in 1)

Soft Peaks: The egg white is starting to turn fluffy with fine bubbles. Yet, it is still moist. It drips when you hold up the electric mixer. Egg white is usually beaten to soft peaks in cheesecakes. The cake won't crack after being baked.(as shown in 2)

Stiff: If the egg white is kept on beaten after the "Soft peaks" stage, it turns thicker and expands in volume. It also gains a satiny sheen. If you hold up your electric mixer at this stage, it does not drip. Egg white is usually beaten until stiff in chiffon cake. It gives the cake a fluffy light texture.(as shown in 3)

蛋白在甜品中佔有重要的位置，經打發的蛋白可以鎖住空氣，在烘焙時可以讓混合料膨脹成漂亮的形狀，在品嘗製成品時的口感又輕、又軟，如梳乎厘；又或與慕思料拌勻，享用時的口感滑如絲。

在這本食譜裏，許多時都會看到將蛋白打發至「起泡」、「濕性發泡」和「乾性發泡」。何謂「起泡」、「濕性發泡」和「乾性發泡」呢？現在讓我解釋一下吧！

起泡：將蛋白略打發，泡沫開始呈現白色，若不繼續打發，泡沫會很易消退。（看圖1）

濕性發泡：蛋白質地開始變厚、柔細，但較濕潤，如用攪拌器捲起蛋白，蛋白會呈下垂狀。濕性發泡的蛋白，多用於烘焙芝士蛋糕，令糕面不會有裂痕。（看圖2）

乾性發泡：如將濕性發泡的蛋白繼續打發，蛋白會變得更加厚，份量會增加，表面有光澤，如用攪拌器捲起蛋白，蛋白不會下垂。乾性發泡蛋白，多用在戚風蛋糕，可令蛋糕的質感軟綿綿。（看圖3）

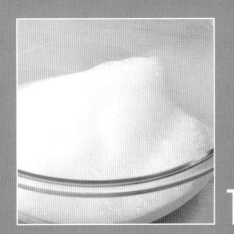

1.

1. Make sure the container and the utensil you use to beat egg white is completely free of oil, water or egg yolk. The presence of any would make the beating process a lot more difficult.

   打發蛋白的容器切忌有油脂、水分和蛋黃,這會令打發效果欠佳。

2. You may add a small amount of cream of tartar into the egg white before beating. Cream of tartar makes the egg white stand more easily by stabilizing the egg white molecules with a weak acid. A little bit of salt or lemon juice works the same way.

   打發蛋白時,加入塔塔粉,可以令打發蛋白的效果更佳;但亦可以用鹽或檸檬汁代替塔塔粉。

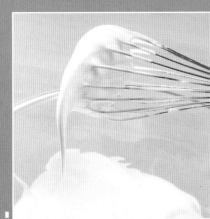

2.

3. Do not beat the eggs on high speed. Use medium speed instead. The foams beaten with high speed do not last and the cake would have a coarse texture after baking.

   不要用高速打發蛋白,宜用中速,否則蛋白的泡沫不會維持太久;同時蛋糕質感會變得粗糙。

4. Adding sugar after the egg white starts to thicken helps stabilize the foams. It also prevents over-beating.

   當蛋白打發至變厚,宜下糖,這可以穩定蛋白的泡沫,同時減低過度打發的機會。

3.

5. Egg white is best beaten in a copper or brass container. A stainless steel bowl would also work fine.

   用銅製容器打發蛋白,效果最佳;其次是用不鏽鋼容器。

CAKE

■

蛋　　糕

You can bake
so many different kinds of cakes
on your own.
The mesmerizing variety and
their beautiful names
can get you drooling.

蛋糕的味道可以千變萬化，
外觀更令人目不暇給，
光聽名字已叫人垂涎三尺！

Rose Pudding Cake
玫瑰布丁蛋糕

Ingredients 材料

Caramel	**焦糖**
50 g sugar	糖 50 克
10 ml water	水 10 毫升
Jelly	**果凍**
200 ml water	水 200 毫升
20 g sugar	糖 20 克
8 g instant jelly powder	果凍粉 8 克
Pudding	**布丁**
100 ml water	水 100 毫升
80 g sugar	糖 80 克
250 ml milk	牛奶 250 毫升
4 eggs	蛋 4 個
10 dried roses	乾玫瑰花 10 朵
Cake	**蛋糕**
40 ml milk	牛奶 40 毫升
40 g butter	牛油 40 克
50 g superfine flour	低筋麵粉 50 克
1/2 tsp vanilla essence	雲尼拿香精 1/2 茶匙
4 egg yolks	蛋黃 4 個
4 egg whites	蛋白 4 個
60 g sugar	糖 60 克
1/4 tsp cream of tartar	塔塔粉 1/4 茶匙

Caramel Jelly

1. Cook sugar from caramel ingredients over low heat until caramelized (as shown in 1). Pour in water and bring to the boil again.
2. Pour in jelly ingredients. Bring to the boil. Pour into jelly mould (as shown in 2). Leave it to set.

Pudding

1. Heat milk up to 80°C. Put in dried roses. Cover for 10 minutes.
2. Stir eggs and sugar gently. Add water and milk. Mix well. Strain. Pour the egg mixture along a spoon over the set jelly (as shown in 3).

Cake

1. Heat milk and butter over low heat until the butter melts. Remove from heat.
2. Stir in superfine flour, egg yolks and vanilla essence.
3. In a seperate bowl, beat egg whites, cream of tartar and sugar at medium speed until soft peaks form.
4. Fold the egg white mixture into the egg yolk mixture. Put the mixture into the piping bag. Pipe the mixture over the pudding mixture (as shown in 4-5).
5. Bake in water bath at 180°C for 1 hour.

焦糖果凍

1. 將焦糖料內的糖用小火煮成焦糖（看圖1），加入水再煮滾。
2. 加入果凍料，煮滾，倒入模內至凝固（看圖2）。

布丁

1. 將牛奶加熱至80℃，加入乾玫瑰花悶10分鐘。
2. 將蛋和糖輕輕拌勻，加入水，與牛奶拌勻，過濾，然後順羹匙倒在果凍上（看圖3）。

蛋糕

1. 將牛奶倒進牛油內，用小火煮溶牛油，離火。
2. 加入低筋麵粉、蛋黃和雲尼拿香精拌勻成蛋黃糊。
3. 蛋白、塔塔粉及糖用中速打發至濕性發泡。
4. 將蛋白糊拌入蛋黃糊內，盛入擠花袋內，然後擠在布丁糊上（看圖4-5）。
5. 以180℃隔水蒸烤1小時。

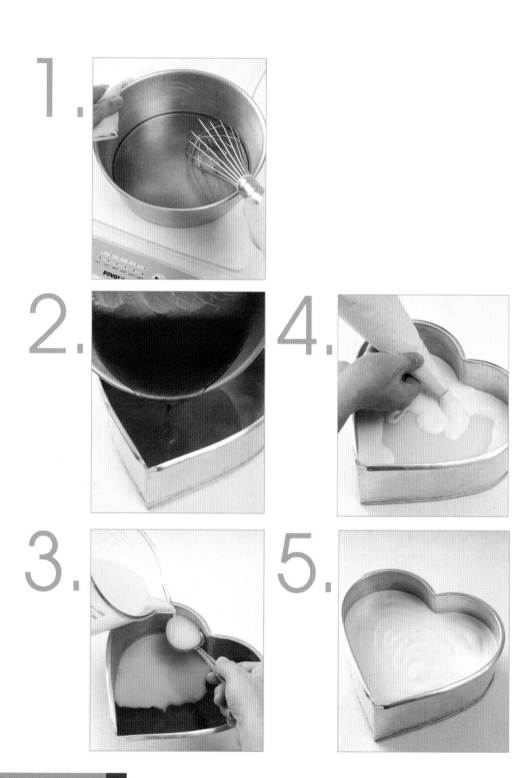

1.

2.

3.

4.

5.

Sesame Burdock Cake

芝麻牛蒡蛋糕

Ingredients 材料

4 egg whites	蛋白 4 個
3 egg yolks	蛋黃 3 個
60 g sugar	糖 60 克
100 g superfine flour	低筋麵粉 100 克
1/4 tsp baking powder	發粉 1/4 茶匙
20 g condensed milk	煉奶 20 克
50 g melted butter	溶化牛油 50 克
50 g dried apricots	杏桃乾 50 克
10 g black sesames	黑芝麻 10 克
50 g burdock	牛蒡 50 克

Method 做法

1. Shred burdock. Cook in water for 10 minutes. Drain.
2. Finely chop dried apricots. Soak in water until soft.
3. Beat egg whites, egg yolks, sugar, superfine flour and baking powder together until fluffy.
4. Pour in condensed milk and combine. Fold in melted butter.
5. Add dried apricots, black sesames and burdock. Mix well.
6. Spoon the batter in cake tins. Bake at 180°C for 15-20 minutes. Serve.

1. 將牛蒡切絲,用水煮 10 分鐘,瀝乾。
2. 杏桃乾切小塊,泡軟。
3. 蛋白、蛋黃、糖、低筋麵粉和發粉一起打發。
4. 加入煉奶拌勻,下牛油,拌勻。
5. 加入杏桃乾、黑芝麻和牛蒡,拌勻。
6. 倒入小烤模內,以 180℃烘焙 15-20 分鐘即可。

Yogurt Chocolate Cake
乳酪朱古力小蛋糕

Ingredients 材料

80 g butter	牛油 80 克
100 g margarine	植物牛油 100 克
70 g sugar	糖 70 克
4 eggs	蛋 4 個
1/2 tsp salt	鹽 1/2 茶匙
100 g yogurt	乳酪 100 克
1 tsp baking powder	發粉 1 茶匙
280 g superfine flour	低筋麵粉 280 克
150 g bittersweet chocolate nuggets	苦朱古力 150 克

Method 做法

1. Beat butter, margarine, salt and sugar together until fluffy.
2. Add one egg at a time. Mix well in between additions.
3. Fold in sifted superfine flour and baking powder.
4. Pour in yogurt and mix well. Add finely chopped chocolate nuggets.
5. Spoon the batter into cake tins. Bake at 180°C for 30-35 minutes.

1. 將牛油、植物牛油、鹽和糖一起打發。
2. 分數次下蛋進牛油糊內，拌勻。
3. 加入已篩的低筋麵粉和發粉，拌勻。
4. 加入乳酪，拌勻，最後加入已切碎的苦朱古力。
5. 將麵糊倒入烤模內，以 180℃ 烤 30-35 分鐘。

Pancake with Custard and Fruit

法式水果煎餅

Ingredients 材料

100 g superfine flour
1/4 tsp salt
3 eggs
1 egg yolk
180 ml milk
70 ml water
25 g melted butter

Filling

3 kiwifruit
20 raspberries
10 strawberries
French custard

低筋麵粉 100 克
鹽 1/4 茶匙
蛋 3 個
蛋黃 1 個
牛奶 180 毫升
水 70 毫升
溶化牛油 25 克

餡料

奇異果 3 粒
覆盆子 20 粒
草莓 10 粒
法式蛋黃醬適量

Method 做法

1. Combine flour, salt, eggs and egg yolks.

2. Pour in milk and water gradually. Mix well.

3. Fold in melted butter. Set aside for 30 minutes.

4. Heat pan. Add a little oil and swirl the pan. Pour some batter and fry on both sides.

5. Spread custard on a pancake. Arrange fruit on top. Put another pancake over the fruit, followed by custard and fruit. Repeat this step until all pancakes are used. Serve.

* The cooking method of French custard, please refer to P. 123.

1. 將麵粉、鹽、蛋和蛋黃一起拌勻。

2. 慢慢加入牛奶和水，拌勻。

3. 再加入溶化牛油，拌勻，靜置 30 分鐘。

4. 將平底鍋燒熱，抹一層油，倒入麵糊煎成薄餅。

5. 在每層薄餅上塗一層法式蛋黃醬，排上新鮮水果，重複這步驟直至用完薄餅。

＊ 法式蛋黃醬製法，請參閱第 123 頁。

Eggless Cake

無蛋蛋糕

Ingredients	材料
1 tsp instant coffee powder	即溶咖啡粉 1 茶匙
60 g sugar	糖 60 克
180 ml milk	牛奶 180 毫升
80 g chocolate	朱古力 80 克
60 g margarine	植物牛油 60 克
150 g superfine flour	低筋麵粉 150 克
1 tsp baking powder	發粉 1 茶匙

Method 做法

1. Heat instant coffee powder, sugar and milk together until instant coffee powder and sugar dissolve.
2. Add chocolate and margarine. Cook until they melt.
3. Remove from heat. Leave it to cool. Add sifted superfine flour and baking powder. Mix well .
4. Spoon into a greased 9-inch cake tin lined with baking paper. Bake at 180°C for 25-30 minutes. Serve.

1. 將即溶咖啡粉、糖和牛奶一起加熱至糖和咖啡粉溶化。
2. 加入朱古力和植物牛油一起煮溶。
3. 離火,待冷,加入已篩的低筋麵粉和發粉拌勻。
4. 倒入已墊紙、塗油的 9 吋烤模內,以 180℃ 烘焙 25-30 分鐘即可。

Blueberry Muffins

藍莓鬆餅

Ingredients 材 料

90 g butter	牛油 90 克
120 g plain flour	麵粉 120 克
1/4 tsp baking powder	發粉 1/4 茶匙
70 g sugar	糖 70 克
1/4 tsp salt	鹽 1/4 茶匙
2 eggs	蛋 2 個
30 ml milk	牛奶 30 毫升
100 g blueberries	藍莓 100 克

1. Sift flour and baking powder together. Add butter and beat until fluffy for about 5 minutes.
2. Put in sugar and salt. Keep beating until fluffy for 2-3 minutes.
3. Add one egg at a time. Mix well after each addition. Beating until smooth. Stir in milk.
4. Add half of the blueberries. Mix gently.
5. Spoon the mixture into greased muffin tins. Place the remaining blueberries on top.
6. Bake at 180°C for 15-20 minutes. Serve.
* Beating butter and flour together helps make the cake more fluffy.

1. 麵粉和發粉一起篩勻，加入牛油一起打發大約 5 分鐘。
2. 加入糖和鹽，繼續打發 2-3 分鐘。
3. 分次加入蛋，攪拌至光滑；加入牛奶，拌勻。
4. 加入一半藍莓，稍微拌勻。
5. 將麵糊倒入已塗油的鬆餅烤模內，上面再放藍莓。
6. 以 180℃烘焙 15-20 分鐘即可。
＊ 麵粉與牛油一起打發，可令蛋糕更鬆軟。

Opera

歌劇院蛋糕

Joconde Biscuit	**久康地蛋糕**
80 g icing sugar	糖粉 80 克
100 g ground almond	杏仁粉 100 克
50 g superfine flour	低筋麵粉 50 克
4 egg yolks	蛋黃 4 個
30 g melted butter	溶化牛油 30 克
4 egg whites	蛋白 4 個
20 g sugar	糖 20 克
Coffee Cream	**咖啡霜飾**
(A) 1 tsp instant coffee powder	(A) 即溶咖啡粉 1 茶匙
10 g sugar	糖 10 克
1 egg white	蛋白 1 個
(B) 2 egg yolks	(B) 蛋黃 2 個
10 g sugar	糖 10 克
(C) 100 g butter	(C) 牛油 100 克
1 tbsp syrup	糖漿 1 湯匙
Ganache	**朱古力霜飾**
200 g cooking chocolate	朱古力 200 克
100 g whipping cream	鮮忌廉 100 克
10 g butter	牛油 10 克

Biscuit

1. Sift icing sugar and ground almond.
2. Add superfine flour, egg yolks and melted butter. Mix well.
3. Beat egg whites and sugar until soft peaks form. Combine egg white mixture with flour mixture.
4. Spoon mixture into an 8-inch cake tin. Bake for 30-40 minutes.

Coffee Cream

1. Whisk (A) in a bowl over simmering water. Beat until fluffy.
2. Whisk (B) in a bowl over simmering water. Beat until light and creamy.
3. Beat (C) until smooth.
4. Combine (A), (B) and (C).

Ganache

Finely chop chocolate. Fold in whipping cream and butter. Melt in a bowl over simmering water. Leave it to cool.

To Assemble

Cut the cake horizontally into 4 layers. Spread coffee cream on one layer. Top with another layer of cake. Brush ganache over it. Repeat the process once more.

蛋糕

1. 將糖粉和杏仁粉一起篩勻。
2. 加入低筋麵粉、蛋黃和溶化牛油拌勻成麵糊。
3. 蛋白和糖一起打發至濕性發泡,加入麵糊內拌勻。
4. 將麵糊倒入8吋烤模內,烘焙30-40分鐘即成。

咖啡霜飾

1. 將(A)一起隔水加熱,打發成咖啡蛋白霜。
2. 將(B)隔熱水打發至變白。
3. 將(C)一起打發至軟滑。
4. 將(A)、(B)和(C)一起拌勻,即成咖啡霜飾。

朱古力霜飾

將朱古力切碎,加入鮮忌廉和牛油一起隔水加熱至朱古力完全溶化,放涼待用。

綜合做法

將蛋糕向橫片成4片,第一層蛋糕塗咖啡霜飾,第二層蛋糕塗朱古力霜飾,第三層蛋糕塗咖啡霜飾,最後一層蛋糕淋上朱古力霜飾即可。

Coconut Pandan Swiss Roll

椰香班蘭卷

Cake

(A)

70 g superfine flour

1/4 tsp baking powder

20 g sugar

1/4 tsp salt

(B)

30 g cooking oil

4 egg yolks

1/2 tsp pandan essence

30 g coconut milk

(C)

4 egg whites

50 g sugar

1/2 tsp cream of tartar

Filling

100 g kaya

蛋糕

(A)

低筋麵粉 70 克

發粉 1/4 茶匙

糖 20 克

鹽 1/4 茶匙

(B)

食油 30 克

蛋黃 4 個

班蘭香精 1/2 茶匙

椰漿 30 克

(C)

蛋白 4 個

糖 50 克

塔塔粉 1/2 茶匙

餡料

咖吔 100 克

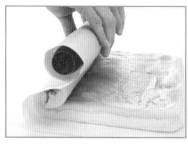

Method 做法

1. Mix superfine flour, baking powder, sugar and salt. Add oil, egg yolks, pandan essence and coconut milk. Stir together into batter.

2. Beat egg whites, sugar and cream of tartar together until soft peaks form. Add the mixture a little at a time to the batter and stir gently.

3. Pour the mixture into 12 x 12-inch baking tray and level the surface. Bake at 180°C for 15 minutes.

To Assemble

1. Make two cuts on the edge of the cake (as shown in 1).

2. Spread kaya over the cake. Roll it up like a Swiss roll (as shown in 2-4). Refrigerate for 30 minutes. Serve.

1. 將低筋麵粉、發粉、糖和鹽拌勻，加入食油、蛋黃、班蘭香精和椰漿一起攪拌均勻。

2. 蛋白、糖和塔塔粉一起打發至濕性發泡，分數次加入麵糊內，輕輕拌勻。

3. 將蛋白麵糊倒入已墊紙的 12 × 12 吋烤盤內，抹平，以 180℃ 烘焙 15 分鐘即可。

綜合做法

1. 在蛋糕邊緣輕輕剠 2 刀（看圖 1）。

2. 在蛋糕表面塗上一層咖吔，捲起成瑞士卷狀（看圖 2-4），放入冰箱冷藏 30 分鐘，即可切件享用。

Strawberry and Rose Soufflé

水果玫瑰梳乎厘

Ingredients 材料

2 egg yolks	蛋黃 2 個
3 egg whites	蛋白 3 個
20 g sugar	糖 20 克
20 g butter	牛油 20 克
15 g superfine flour	低筋麵粉 15 克
5 dried roses	乾玫瑰 5 朵
2 strawberries	草莓 2 粒
130 ml milk	牛奶 130 毫升

Method 做法

1. Melt butter over low heat. Add flour and cook for 1 minute. Remove from heat.
2. Pour in milk and mix well. Bring to the boil again. Remove from heat.
3. Add dried roses and cover the lid for a few minutes. Leave it to cool.
4. Add egg yolks and mix well.
5. In a separate bowl, beat egg whites and sugar until soft peaks form. Fold in the egg yolk mixture from step (4).
6. Put strawberries into greased soufflé dish. Spoon the mixture into soufflé dish.
7. Bake at 190°C for 20 minutes. Serve hot.

1. 用小火煮溶牛油，加入麵粉繼續煮一分鐘，離火。
2. 加入牛奶拌勻，再加熱至滾，離火。
3. 加入乾玫瑰悶幾分鐘，待涼。
4. 加入蛋黃，拌勻。
5. 將蛋白和糖打發至濕性發泡，加入(4)內，拌勻。
6. 在梳乎厘杯內塗油，放入草莓，倒入麵糊。
7. 以 190℃烘焙 20 分鐘，趁熱享用。

Prune Tea Cake
黑棗紅茶蛋糕

Ingredients 材料

(A)	(A)
3 eggs	蛋 3 個
80 g sugar	糖 80 克
(B)	**(B)**
100 g dried prunes	乾黑棗 100 克
1/2 tsp baking soda	小蘇打 1/2 茶匙
80 ml hot tea	熱茶 80 毫升
(C)	**(C)**
150 g plain flour	麵粉 150 克
50 g walnuts (toasted)	核桃 50 克（烤香）
(D)	**(D)**
30 g melted butter	溶化牛油 30 克

Method 做法

1. Pit and finely chop prunes. Pour in hot tea and baking soda. Soak for 2 hours.
2. Beat the ingredients (A) for 10-15 minutes until thickens.
3. Pour in tea with prunes and mix well. Sift the plain flour in and fold it into the prune mixture. Pour in melted butter and roasted walnuts. Stir gently.
4. Spoon into a 9-inch cake tin. Bake at 170-180°C for 30 minutes.

1. 將黑棗切小塊，加入熱茶和小蘇打中泡 2 小時。
2. 將材料（A）打發大約 10-15 分鐘至蛋成濃稠狀。
3. 加入黑棗和熱茶，拌勻。加入已篩的麵粉，拌勻；最後加入溶化牛油和核桃輕輕拌勻。
4. 麵糊倒入 9 吋烤模內，以 170-180℃烘焙 30 分鐘。

Nutritious Cake

養生蛋糕

Ingredients 材料

(A)
40 g olive oil or cooking oil
60 ml milk

(B)
100 g superfine flour
1 egg white

(C)
5 egg whites
70 g sugar

(D)
1 tbsp Gou Qi Xi
10 red dates
1 tbsp flaxseeds
1 tbsp sunflower seeds
1 tbsp pumpkin seeds
1 tbsp oats

(A)
橄欖油／食油 40 克
牛奶 60 毫升

(B)
低筋麵粉 100 克
蛋白 1 個

(C)
蛋白 5 個
糖 70 克

(D)
枸杞子 1 湯匙
紅棗 10 粒
亞麻籽 1 湯匙
太陽花籽 1 湯匙
南瓜籽 1 湯匙
燕麥片 1 湯匙

Method 做法

1. Finely chop red dates. Soak red dates and Gou Qi Xi in water together. Drain.

2. Heat olive oil and milk together up to 50°C. Remove from heat. Fold in sifted superfine flour and 1 egg white.

3. Put in red dates, Gou Qi Xi, flaxseeds, sunflower seeds, pumpkin seeds and oats. Mix well.

4. In a separate bowl, beat egg whites and sugar until soft peaks form. Add the flour mixture and stir gently.

5. Spoon into a greased 7-inch cake tin lined with baking paper. Bake at 180°C for 25 minutes or until done. Serve.

1. 紅棗切小塊，和枸杞子一起泡水，濾乾。

2. 將橄欖油和牛奶一起加熱至 50℃，離火，加入已篩低筋麵粉和一個蛋白，拌勻。

3. 加入紅棗、枸杞子、亞麻籽、太陽花籽、南瓜籽和燕麥片拌勻。

4. 蛋白加糖打發至濕性發泡，加入麵糊內輕輕拌勻。

5. 將麵糊倒入 7 吋已墊紙、塗油的烤模內，以 180℃烘焙 25 分鐘至熟即可。

Earl Grey Tea Cake
伯爵紅茶蛋糕

Cake
5 g earl grey tea leaves
4 eggs
120 g sugar
50 ml milk
100 g superfine flour
20 g melted butter

Earl Grey Tea Cream
5 g earl grey tea leaves
100 g whipping cream
100 g non-dairy whipped topping

蛋糕
伯爵紅茶 5 克
蛋 4 個
糖 120 克
牛奶 50 毫升
低筋麵粉 100 克
溶化牛油 20 克

伯爵紅茶忌廉霜
伯爵紅茶 5 克
鮮忌廉 100 克
植物性鮮忌廉 100 克

Method 做法

Cake

1. Grind earl grey tea leaves.
2. Heat eggs, sugar and ground earl grey tea leaves together in a hot water bath up to 40°C. Beat until fluffy.
3. Sift superfine flour. Add flour to the egg mixture. Fold in gently.
4. Add milk and mix well. Pour in melted butter and mix well. Spoon into cake tin. Bake at 180°C for 30 minutes until done.

Earl Grey Tea Cream

1. Heat earl grey tea leaves and whipping cream together. Remove from heat and cover the lid for 10 minutes. Leave it to cool.
2. Add non-dairy whipped topping and beat together until fluffy.

To Assemble

Cut the cake horizontally into 3 layers. Sandwich the earl grey tea cream in between the cake layers. Coat the whole cake in the cream.

蛋糕

1. 將伯爵紅茶磨碎。
2. 將蛋、糖和伯爵紅茶一起隔水加熱至40℃，再打發。
3. 篩入低筋麵粉，輕輕拌勻。
4. 注入牛奶拌勻，加入溶化牛油，拌勻。將麵糊倒入烤模內，以 180℃烘焙 30 分鐘至熟即可。

伯爵紅茶忌廉霜

1. 將伯爵紅茶和鮮忌廉一起加熱，離火，悶約 10 分鐘，待涼。
2. 加入植物性鮮忌廉一起打發即成。

綜合做法

將蛋糕向橫片成 3 片，用伯爵紅茶忌廉霜夾層及塗勻整個蛋糕即可。

Beancurd Cake
豆腐蛋糕

(A)
60 g soybean milk, 40 g cooking oil
(B)
100 g superfine flour, 1 egg white
(C)
5 egg whites, 80 g sugar
(D)
50 g sweetened cooked red beans
Garnish
200 g non-dairy whipped topping
50 g sweetened cooked red beans

(A)
豆漿 60 克，食油 40 克
(B)
低筋麵粉 100 克，蛋白 1 個
(C)
蛋白 5 個，糖 80 克
(D)
蜜紅豆 50 克
裝飾
植物性鮮忌廉 200 克
蜜紅豆 50 克

Method | 做法

1. Preheat oven to 180°C.
2. Heat (A) up to 80°C until it turns white completely.
3. Add (B). Mix well.
4. Beat 5 egg whites until light and creamy. Add sugar and stir moderately until soft peaks form.
5. Pour the egg white mixture to the soybean milk mixture. Stir gently. Spoon the mixture into a 8-inch cake tin which is greased and lined with baking paper.
6. Add cooked red beans and stir gently. Bake at 180°C for 30 minutes.

To Assemble

Cut the cake horizontally into 4 layers. Sandwich the filling in between cake layers. Coat the whole cake with non-dairy whipped topping. Garnish with cooked red beans.

1. 預熱烤爐 180℃。
2. 將(A)一起煮熱至大約 80℃，直至完全呈白色。
3. 加入(B)拌勻。
4. 將 5 個蛋白打發至起泡，加入糖，以中速打發至濕性發泡。
5. 將蛋白倒入麵糊中輕輕拌勻，倒入已塗油、鋪紙的 8 吋模子內。
6. 最後加入蜜紅豆，稍微拌一拌，以 180℃烤 30 分鐘。

綜合做法

蛋糕向橫片成4片，每一片塗上已打發的鮮忌廉和紅豆夾心，再整個塗上一層薄薄的鮮忌廉，再綴上蜜紅豆即成。

Savarin

薩瓦蘭

10 g instant yeast	即溶酵母 10 克
30 ml warm water	溫水 30 毫升
300 g high gluten flour	高筋麵粉 300 克
25 g sugar	糖 25 克
250 g eggs	蛋 250 克
60 ml milk	牛奶 60 毫升
3 g salt	鹽 3 克
100 g unsalted butter	無鹽牛油 100 克
Sauce	**果醬糖漿**
50 g sugar	糖 50 克
250 ml water	水 250 毫升
1 tea bag	紅茶包 1 個
200 g strawberry puree	草莓果泥 200 克
juice from 1 orange	香橙 1 個（榨汁）
Garnish	**裝飾**
fresh fruit	新鮮水果適量
French custard	法式蛋黃醬適量
strawberry jam	草莓醬適量

Method | 做法

1. Mix yeast with warm water. Leave it for 10 minutes.
2. Add flour, sugar, salt, milk and eggs. Mix well. Let dough prove for 1 hour. Add butter and mix well.
3. Pipe dough into greased Savarin tins. Leave it for 30 minutes until dough grows twice in size (as shown in 1a, 1b is the dough before proving). Bake at 180°C for 30 minutes. Set aside.
4. Heat the sauce ingredients up to 60°C. Cut the bottom off baked Savarin. Soak in the sauce for 30 minutes (turn the Savarin upside down once in the process) (as shown in 2-3).
5. Remove Savarin and leave it on a wire rack overnight (as shown in 4).
6. Pipe strawberry jam onto plate. Put Savarin over the jam. Serve with French custard and fresh fruit.
* For the cooking method of French custard, please refer to P. 123.

1. 將酵母和溫水調勻，靜置 10 分鐘。
2. 加入高筋麵粉、糖、鹽、牛奶和蛋一起攪拌均勻，讓麵糰發酵 1 小時，加入牛油再攪拌均勻。
3. 將麵糰擠入已塗油的薩瓦蘭烤模內，放置 30 分鐘，待發酵至雙倍大（看圖 1 的 a，b 是未發酵的麵糰），以 180℃烤 30 分鐘，待用。
4. 將果醬糖漿的材料一起加熱至 60℃，將烤熟的薩瓦蘭切去底部，然後浸在果醬糖漿內 30 分鐘（期間須反轉浸泡）（看圖 2-3）。
5. 將薩瓦蘭撈起，放在架子上一夜（看圖 4）。
6. 在碟子上擠草莓醬，再放薩瓦蘭；擠上法式蛋黃醬，配新鮮水果一起享用。
＊ 法式蛋黃醬製法，請參閱第 123 頁。

Caramel Cake

焦糖蛋糕

材 料

Ingredients	材 料
Cake	**蛋糕**
100 g butter	牛油 100 克
60 g cooking chocolate (melted)	烹調朱古力 60 克（煮溶）
1/2 tsp vanilla essence	雲尼拿香精 1/2 茶匙
1/4 tsp salt	鹽 1/4 茶匙
5 egg yolks	蛋黃 5 個
4 egg whites	蛋白 4 個
100 g sugar	糖 100 克
1/4 tsp cream of tartar	塔塔粉 1/4 茶匙
90 g superfine flour	低筋麵粉 90 克
Caramel Cream	**焦糖忌廉**
80 g sugar	糖 80 克
20 g glucose syrup	葡萄糖漿 20 克
150 g whipping cream	鮮忌廉 150 克
20 g butter	牛油 20 克
Chocolate Sauce	**朱古力醬**
150 g whipping cream	鮮忌廉 150 克
200 g cooking chocolate	烹調朱古力 200 克

>>044

cake>>

1. Beat butter until soft. Pour in melted chocolate. Stir in vanilla essence, salt and egg yolks.
2. Beat egg whites, cream of tartar and sugar at medium speed until soft peaks form. Fold the egg white mixture into the egg yolk mixture.
3. Spoon into three 8-inch round cake tins separately. Bake at 180°C for 10-15 minutes.

Caramel Cream

1. Cook sugar and glucose syrup in a sauce pan until golden brown. Pour in whipping cream and butter. Bring to the boil. Remove from heat and leave it to cool.
2. Refrigerate. Remove from fridge and beat until fluffy.

Chocolate Sauce

1. Melt chocolate with sugar in a small bowl over simmering water. Remove from heat and refrigerate.
2. Remove from fridge and beat until fluffy. Set aside.

To Assemble

Cut the cake horizontally into 3 layers. Spread caramel cream over one layer of cake and spread chocolate sauce over the caramel cream. Cover it with second layer of cake. Repeat the previous step of spreading caramel and chocolate sauce. Top with third layer of cake. Cover the top layer of cake in chocolate sauce first and then caramel cream.

1. 將牛油打軟，加入溶化朱古力，拌勻。加入雲尼拿香精、鹽和蛋黃拌勻成蛋黃糊。
2. 蛋白、塔塔粉及糖用中速打發至濕性發泡，將蛋白拌入蛋黃糊內。
3. 分別倒入3個8吋圓模內，以180℃烘焙10-15分鐘。

焦糖忌廉

1. 將糖和葡萄糖漿放入鍋內煮至金黃色，倒入鮮忌廉和牛油再煮至滾，離火，待涼。
2. 放入冰箱冷凍，取出打發。

朱古力醬

1. 鮮忌廉和朱古力一起隔熱水溶化，放入冰箱冷藏。
2. 取出打發，待用。

綜合做法

蛋糕向橫片3片，底層蛋糕片塗一層焦糖忌廉和一層朱古力醬；第二層蛋糕片塗一層焦糖忌廉和一層朱古力醬，面層蛋糕先塗一層朱古力醬，然後塗上焦糖忌廉。

Chocolate Soufflé

朱古力梳乎厘

2 egg yolks	蛋黃 2 個
3 egg whites	蛋白 3 個
1/4 tsp cream of tartar	塔塔粉 1/4 茶匙
20 g sugar	糖 20 克
20 g butter	牛油 20 克
15 g superfine flour	低筋麵粉 15 克
130 ml milk	牛奶 130 毫升
50 g melted chocolate	朱古力 50 克（溶化）

Method 做法

1. Melt butter over low heat. Pour in flour and cook for 1 minute. Remove from heat.
2. Pour in milk and mix well. Bring to the boil again. Add chocolate and mix. Remove from heat and leave it to cool.
3. Fold in egg yolks.
4. In a separate bowl, beat egg whites, sugar and cream of tartar until soft peaks form. Add egg yolk mixture from step (3) and fold in well.
5. Spoon the mixture into greased soufflé dish. Bake at 190°C for 20 minutes. Serve immediately.

1. 用小火煮溶牛油，加入麵粉繼續煮一分鐘，離火。
2. 加入牛奶拌勻，再加熱至滾，加入朱古力拌勻，離火，待涼。
3. 加入蛋黃，拌勻。
4. 將蛋白、糖及塔塔粉打發至濕性發泡，倒進（3）內拌勻。
5. 將混合物舀進已塗油的梳乎厘杯內，以190℃烘焙 20 分鐘，趁熱享用。

Red Bean Green Tea Cake
紅豆綠茶蛋糕

40 g butter	牛油 40 克
80 ml milk	牛奶 80 毫升
70 g superfine flour	低筋麵粉 70 克
1/4 tsp baking powder	發粉 1/4 茶匙
5 g green tea powder	綠茶粉 5 克
4 egg yolks	蛋黃 4 個
5 egg whites	蛋白 5 個
50 g sugar	糖 50 克
Filling	**餡料**
120 g whipping cream	鮮忌廉 120 克
100 g sweetened cooked red beans	蜜紅豆 100 克
Garnish	**裝飾**
green tea powder	綠茶粉少許

Method 做法

1. Heat butter and milk up to 50°C. Remove from heat.
2. Add sifted superfine flour, green tea powder and baking powder. Mix well. Stir in egg yolks.
3. In a separate bowl, beat egg whites and sugar until soft peaks form. Add the egg white mixture to the batter mixture a little at a time. Fold in well after each addition.
4. Pour into 14 x 14-inch baking tray. Bake at 180°C for 15 minutes or until done.

To Assemble

Cut the cake horizontally into 4 layers. Sandwich the filling in between cake layers. Coat the top layer with more whipped cream. Dust the top with green tea powder. Serve.

1. 將牛油和牛奶加熱至大約 50℃，離火。
2. 加入已篩勻的麵粉、綠茶粉和發粉，拌勻；再加入蛋黃，拌勻。
3. 蛋白和糖打發至濕性發泡，分次加入麵糊內，拌勻。
4. 將麵糊倒入 14 × 14 吋的烤盤內，以 180℃ 烘焙 15 分鐘至熟即可。

綜合做法

將蛋糕向橫片成 4 片，塗抹已打發的鮮忌廉、撒上蜜紅豆，夾層，蛋糕面塗上薄薄的忌廉，再灑綠茶粉即可。

Supreme Dark Chocolate Cake

純朱古力蛋糕

Ingredients 材料

150 g cooking chocolate	烹調朱古力 150 克
80 g butter	牛油 80 克
3 egg whites	蛋白 3 個
3 egg yolks	蛋黃 3 個
30 g sugar	糖 30 克

Method 做法

1. Melt butter and chocolate in a bowl over simmering water. Leave it to cool.
2. Add egg yolks and mix well.
3. In a separate bowl, beat egg whites and sugar together until soft peaks form. Fold half of the egg white mixture into the chocolate mixture. Stir gently. Fold in the rest of the egg white mixture.
4. Spoon into greased cake tin. Bake at 180°C for 25-30 minutes. Serve.

1. 將牛油和朱古力隔熱水溶化，待涼。
2. 加入蛋黃，拌勻。
3. 將蛋白和糖一起打發至濕性發泡，分兩次加入朱古力糊內，輕輕拌勻。
4. 然後倒進已塗油的烤模內，以 180℃ 烘焙 25-30 分鐘即可。

Sweet Potato Cake

番薯蛋糕

Ingredients 材料

120 g butter	牛油 120 克
140 g superfine flour	低筋麵粉 140 克
1/3 tsp baking powder	發粉 1/3 茶匙
80 g sugar	糖 80 克
1/2 tsp salt	鹽 1/2 茶匙
2 eggs	蛋 2 個
200 g steamed sweet potatoes (mashed)	蒸熟番薯（壓爛）200 克
40 g raisins	葡萄乾 40 克

Method 做法

1. Beat butter until soft. Fold in sifted superfine flour and baking powder. Whisk until fluffy.
2. Add sugar and salt. Stir for another 2-3 minutes.
3. Add one egg at a time. Beat well after each addition.
4. Put in steamed sweet potatoes and raisins.
5. Spoon batter into cake tins. Bake at 180°C for 20-25 minutes or until done. Serve.

1. 將牛油打發至軟，加入已篩的低筋麵粉和發粉，一起攪拌至鬆發。
2. 加入糖和鹽再攪拌 2-3 分鐘。
3. 蛋分次加入，慢慢拌勻。
4. 最後加入番薯茸和葡萄乾。
5. 將麵糊倒入烤模內，以 180℃ 烘烤 20-25 分鐘至熟即可。

Blueberry and Cherry Cake
藍莓櫻桃蛋糕

Ingredients 材料

(A)
20 g cocoa powder, 60 ml warm water
(B)
100 g superfine flour
1/2 tsp baking powder, 40 g sugar
(C)
30 g melted butter
4 egg yolks, 30 ml milk
(D)
4 egg whites, 40 g sugar
1/6 tsp cream of tartar
Syrup
50 ml cherry juice, 1 tsp sugar
Garnish
150 g whipping cream
dark pitted cherries, blueberries
white chocolate

(A)
可可粉 20 克，溫水 60 毫升
(B)
低筋麵粉 100 克，發粉 1/2 茶匙
糖 40 克
(C)
溶化牛油 30 克，蛋黃 4 個
牛奶 30 毫升
(D)
蛋白 4 個，糖 40 克，塔塔粉 1/6 茶匙
糖漿
櫻桃汁 50 毫升，糖 1 茶匙
裝飾
鮮忌廉 150 克，黑櫻桃適量，藍莓適量
白朱古力適量

Method | 做法

1. Mix cocoa powder and water until cocoa powder dissolves.
2. Sift superfine flour and baking powder together. Add sugar and mix well.
3. Pour in melted butter, egg yolks, milk and dissolved cocoa powder. Stir with an egg whisk.
4. Beat egg whites, sugar and cream of tartar together until stiff peaks form. Add half of the egg whites at a time to the cocoa powder mixture. Fold gently after each addition.
5. Spoon the mixture into a greased 8-inch cake tin. Bake at 180°C for 30-35 minutes.

To Assemble

1. Cut the cake horizontally into 3 layers.
2. Add sugar to cherry juice. Boil until sugar dissolves. This is the syrup. Brush syrup on each layer of cake.
3. Beat whipping cream until fluffy. Spread cream on the layer of cake. Arrange cherries on top. Place another layer of cake on top.
4. Spread cream on the top layer of cake. Arrange blueberries on top.
5. Top with a layer of cake. Sprinkle white chocolate on top.

1. 溫水和可可粉調勻。
2. 將低筋麵粉和發粉一起篩勻，加入糖拌勻。
3. 加入溶化牛油、蛋黃、牛奶和已調勻的可可粉水，一起用打蛋器攪拌均勻。
4. 蛋白、糖和塔塔粉一起打發至乾性發泡，將蛋白分兩次加入麵糊內輕輕拌勻。
5. 將麵糊倒入已塗油的8吋烤模內，用180℃烘焙30-35分鐘。

綜合做法

1. 將蛋糕向橫片成3片。
2. 櫻桃汁內下糖，待糖煮溶即成糖漿；在每片蛋糕上掃糖漿。
3. 蛋糕表面塗上一層已打發的鮮忌廉，放上黑櫻桃，再蓋上一層蛋糕。
4. 再塗一層鮮忌廉，放上藍莓。
5. 最後再蓋上一層蛋糕，灑上白朱古力即成。

Low-sugar Fruit Cake
低糖水果蛋糕

(A)	**(A)**
30 g sugar	糖 30 克
1/2 tsp salt	鹽 1/2 茶匙
30 g olive oil	橄欖油 30 克
50 g honey	蜂蜜 50 克
50 g raisins	葡萄乾 50 克
100 g dried apricot	杏桃乾 100 克
100 g pineapple	菠蘿 100 克
250 ml water or pineapple syrup	水／罐頭菠蘿水 250 毫升
1 tsp ground cinnamon	肉桂粉 1 茶匙
(B)	**(B)**
200 g high gluten flour	高筋麵粉 200 克
1 tsp baking powder	發粉 1 茶匙
1/2 tsp baking soda	小蘇打 1/2 茶匙
(C)	**(C)**
pumpkin seeds	南瓜籽適量
sesames	芝麻適量
sunflower seeds	太陽花籽適量

Method 做法

1. Mix the ingredients (A) in a big stainless steel pot. Bring to the boil over medium heat. Reduce to low heat and cook for 5 more minutes. Remove from heat. Leave it to cool.
2. Fold in sifted ingredients (B).
3. Add the ingredients (C). Mix well. Spoon into cake tin. Bake at 180°C for 30-35 minutes.

1. 將材料(A)混合在大不銹鋼盆內，用中火煮滾，改調小火繼續煮 5 分鐘，離火，待涼。
2. 加入已篩的材料(B)，拌勻。
3. 加入材料(C)，拌勻，倒入烤模內，以180℃烤 30-35 分鐘。

Soft Cake with Jackfruit

菠蘿蜜蒸蛋糕

Ingredients 材料

2 eggs	蛋 2 個
80 g sugar	糖 80 克
1 tsp cake emulsifier	蛋糕乳化劑 1 茶匙
200 g superfine flour	低筋麵粉 200 克
1 tsp baking powder	發粉 1 茶匙
120 ml milk	牛奶 120 毫升
200 g jackfruit (cut into pieces)	菠蘿蜜（切小塊）200 克

Method 做法

1. Combine eggs and sugar gently. Add cake emulsifier, flour, baking powder and milk. Beat together for 5 minutes or until the mixture is fluffy.
2. Put in jackfruit and mix well.
3. Spoon into greased cake tin. Steam over medium heat for 20 minutes. Serve.

1. 蛋和糖稍微拌勻，加入蛋糕乳化劑、麵粉、發粉和牛奶一起打發，大約 5 分鐘，至麵糊濃稠光滑即可。
2. 加入菠蘿蜜，拌勻。
3. 將麵糊倒入已塗油的模子內，以中火蒸 20 分鐘即可。

MOUSSE • PUDDING

■

慕 思 • 布 丁

How do you choose between
silky smooth mousse and
velvety pudding? But why did you
have to choose in the first place?
With our low-sugar recipes,
you can always have them all.

滑如絲的慕思、香甜柔滑的布丁,兩
者各有特色、各具風味,
你較喜歡哪一種呢? 很難選擇?
不要緊,就一次過品嘗它們吧!

Taro Mousse Trifle
芋頭慕思

300 g steamed taro (mashed)	蒸熟芋頭 300 克（搗爛）
200 ml milk	牛奶 200 毫升
60 g sugar	糖 60 克
30 ml water	水 30 毫升
2 egg whites	蛋白 2 個
200 g whipping cream	鮮忌廉 200 克
10 g gelatine	明膠粉 10 克
30 ml hot water	熱水 30 毫升
1 slice sponge cake (cut into pieces)	海綿蛋糕 1 大片（切小片）

Method 做法

1. Dissolve gelatine in hot water. Bring sugar and water to the boil to make hot syrup.
2. Beat egg whites until soft peaks form. Add hot syrup and beat further until fluffy. Beat whipping cream until soft peaks form.
3. Mix milk with mashed taro. Pour in dissolved gelatine and combine.
4. Fold in egg white mixture. Add whipped cream.

To Assemble
Pour a layer of mousse on the bottom of the glass first. Then put a piece of cake over the mousse. Repeat the process until all the mousse and cake is used up. Refrigerate until set. Serve.

1. 將明膠粉加熱水，拌溶。將糖和水一起煮滾成熱糖漿。
2. 蛋白打發至濕性發泡，加入熱糖漿一起打發。鮮忌廉打發至發泡。
3. 牛奶加入芋頭泥內拌勻，下溶化明膠拌勻。
4. 加入已打發的蛋白糖霜，拌勻，最後加入打發鮮忌廉。

綜合做法
先倒一層慕思進玻璃杯內，再鋪一片蛋糕，重複做法，直至完成，置冰箱冷凍至凝固，即可品嘗。

Lavender Mousse Cake
薰衣草慕思蛋糕

Ingredients 材料

15 g gelatine	明膠粉 15 克
50 ml water	水 50 毫升
150 ml milk	牛奶 150 毫升
1 tbsp lavender	薰衣草 1 湯匙
60 g sugar	糖 60 克
2 egg yolks	蛋黃 2 個
200 g whipping cream	鮮忌廉 200 克
pithless mandarin orange	柑肉適量
1 slice sponge cake	海綿蛋糕 1 片

Method 做法

1. Put gelatine in water. Heat it in a small bowl over simmering water until gelatine dissolves.
2. Heat milk up to 80°C. Remove from heat. Put in lavender. Cover the lid and leave it for 10 minutes.
3. Add dissolved gelatine and combine well.
4. In a separate bowl, beat egg yolks and sugar until fluffy. Stir over a hot water bath until satiny. Remove from heat. Add the milk mixture from step (3). Mix well. Add pithless mandarin orange.
5. Beat whipping cream until fluffy. Add whipped cream to the egg yolk mixture and combine well.
6. Put a slice of sponge cake on the bottom of the cake tin. Spoon the batter into cake tin. Refrigerate for 4 hours. Serve.

1. 將明膠粉和水調勻，隔熱水溶化。
2. 牛奶加熱至 80℃，離火，加入薰衣草，悶 10 分鐘。
3. 加入已溶化的明膠粉，拌勻。
4. 打發蛋黃和糖，隔水加熱，一邊攪拌至光滑，離火，加入 (3)，拌勻；再下柑肉。
5. 打發鮮忌廉，加入混合料內拌勻。
6. 慕思模底部墊蛋糕，倒入慕思，放入冰箱冷凍 4 小時即可。

Durian Panna Cotta

榴槤奶酪

(A)
600 ml milk
80 g whipping cream
60 g sugar
(B)
15 g gelatine
60 ml water
200 g durian puree

（A）
牛奶 600 毫升
鮮忌廉 80 克
糖 60 克
（B）
明膠粉 15 克
水 60 毫升
榴槤果肉 200 克

1. Add gelatine to water.
2. Cook ingredients (A) until sugar dissolves. Add gelatine solution and stir until gelatine dissolves.
3. Add durian puree and mix well. Strain. Spoon into pudding cups. Set aside and let cool. Refrigerate for 2 hours. Serve.

1. 將明膠粉和水調勻。
2. 將材料（A）一起煮至糖溶解，加入明膠粉溶液。
3. 下榴槤果肉拌勻，過濾，倒入杯內，待涼，放入冰箱冷藏 2 小時即可食用。

Red Bean Mousse Cake

紅豆慕思蛋糕

Ingredients 材料

Mousse

300 g sweetened cooked red beans
50 g sugar
15 g gelatine
30 ml water
250 g whipping cream
250 ml milk
1 slice sponge cake

Jelly

5 g gelatine
150 ml water
100 g sweetened cooked red beans

慕思

蜜紅豆 300 克
糖 50 克
明膠粉 15 克
水 30 毫升
鮮忌廉 250 克
牛奶 250 毫升
海綿蛋糕一片

果凍

明膠粉 5 克
水 150 毫升
蜜紅豆 100 克

Method 做法

Mousse

1. Put gelatine and water in a bowl. Heat over simmering water until gelatine dissolves.
2. Heat milk up to 80°C. Remove from heat. Add dissolved gelatine and mix well. Add sweetened cooked red beans.
3. In a separate bowl, beat whipping cream until fluffy. Add whipped cream to red bean mixture and fold in.
4. Place sponge cake on the bottom of a cake tin. Spoon mousse over sponge cake. Refrigerate for 4 hours.

Jelly

Put gelatine and water in a bowl. Heat over simmering water until gelatine dissolves. Pour over set mousse. Sprinkle red beans on top.

Sweetened Red Beans

Soak red beans in water for 3 hours. Cook in water until soft. Add suitable amount of sugar and cook until sugar dissolves.

慕思

1. 將明膠粉和水拌勻,隔熱水溶化。
2. 牛奶和糖加熱至80℃,離火,加入已溶化的明膠,拌勻,加入蜜紅豆。
3. 打發鮮忌廉,倒入混合料內。
4. 慕思模底部墊蛋糕,倒入慕思,放入冰箱冷凍4小時即可。

果凍

將明膠粉和水混合,隔熱水加熱至明膠粉完全溶化,倒在慕思表面,撒上蜜紅豆即可。

蜜紅豆

將紅豆泡水3小時,加入水煮至軟,加入適量糖,待糖煮溶即可。

Beancurd Mousse

豆腐慕思蛋糕

Ingredients 材料

1 slice sponge cake	海綿蛋糕 1 片
150 g cream cheese	忌廉芝士 150 克
30 g sugar	糖 30 克
70 ml soybean milk	豆漿 70 毫升
8 g gelatine	明膠粉 8 克
30 ml water	水 30 毫升
100 g whipping cream	鮮忌廉 100 克
blueberry sauce	藍莓醬適量

Method 做法

1. Line the bottom of a cake tin with sponge cake.
2. Put gelatine with water in a small bowl. Heat over simmering water until gelatine dissolves.
3. Beat cream cheese and sugar until smooth and lump-free. Pour in soybean milk and mix well. Add dissolved gelatine and fold in.
4. In a separate bowl, beat whipping cream until fluffy. Add cream to the cream cheese mixture from step (3). Spoon the mixture into cake tin.
5. Refrigerate for 4 hours. Serve with blueberry sauce on the side.

1. 將蛋糕墊在慕思模內。
2. 明膠粉加水拌勻,隔熱水加熱至溶化。
3. 將忌廉芝士和糖打發至沒有顆粒呈光滑狀,加入豆漿拌勻,再加入已溶化的明膠粉水。
4. 打發鮮忌廉,加入以上的混合料內拌勻,然後倒入慕思模內。
5. 冷藏 4 小時,可以伴上藍莓醬一起食用。

Cappuccino Mousse

卡布基諾慕思

Ingredients 材料

20 g gelatine	明膠粉 20 克
60 ml warm water	溫水 60 毫升
60 g sugar	糖 60 克
150 ml milk	牛奶 150 毫升
25 g cappuccino coffee powder	卡布基諾粉 25 克
200 g cream cheese	忌廉芝士 200 克
150 g whipping cream	鮮忌廉 150 克

Method 做法

1. Dissolve gelatine in warm water.
2. Beat cream cheese and sugar until smooth. Add dissolved gelatine.
3. Pour in milk and cappuccino coffee powder. Combine. Beat whipping cream until fluffy. Add cream to cappuccino mixture.
4. Spoon into cups. Refrigerate for 4 hours. Serve.

1. 明膠粉用溫水調勻至溶化。
2. 芝士加糖攪拌至光滑，下已溶化的明膠粉。
3. 加入牛奶和卡布基諾粉，拌勻；加入已打發的鮮忌廉。
4. 將慕思倒入杯子內，放入冰箱冷凍4小時即可享用。

Sour Sop Mousse
紅毛榴槤慕思

(A)
15 g gelatine
50 ml hot water
(B)
40 g sugar
30 ml water
(C)
2 egg whites
(D)
2 egg yolks
40 g sugar
200 ml milk
(E)
250 g whipping cream
(F)
300 g sour sop puree
1 slice sponge cake

(A)
明膠粉 15 克
熱水 50 毫升
(B)
糖 40 克
水 30 毫升
(C)
蛋白 2 個
(D)
蛋黃 2 個
糖 40 克
牛奶 200 毫升
(E)
鮮忌廉 250 克
(F)
紅毛榴槤果泥 300 克
海綿蛋糕 1 片

1. Add hot water to gelatine and mix well. Heat in a bowl over simmering water until gelatine dissolves.
2. Boil sugar and water until it thickens like syrup. Beat egg whites until soft peaks form. Add syrup and beat further until fluffy.
3. Beat egg yolks and sugar over a hot water bath until pale. Pour in milk and keep on heating briefly. Remove from heat.
4. Add dissolved gelatine and mix well. Add beaten egg white and mix well. Leave it to cool. Put in sour sop puree and whipping cream.
5. Line the bottom of the mould with sponge cake. Pour mousse over cake. Refrigerate for 4 hours. Serve.

1. 將明膠粉加熱水拌勻，隔熱水溶化。
2. 將(B)一起煮滾成熱糖漿；蛋白打發至濕性發泡，加入熱糖漿一起打發。
3. 蛋黃和糖隔熱水打發至變白，加入牛奶繼續隔水加熱，離火。
4. 加入溶化魚膠粉，拌勻。下已打發的蛋白，拌勻，待冷。再加入果泥和已打發的鮮忌廉。
5. 杯內先墊一層蛋糕，倒入慕思，放入冰箱冷藏 4 小時即可享用。

Caramel Coffee Mousse

焦糖咖啡慕思

Ingredients 材料

120 g sugar	糖 120 克
300 g whipping cream	鮮忌廉 300 克
100 g coconut milk	椰漿 100 克
3 egg yolks	蛋黃 3 個
80 g chocolate	朱古力 80 克
10 g gelatine	明膠粉 10 克
30 ml water	水 30 毫升
1 tsp instant coffee powder	即溶咖啡粉 1 茶匙
1 slice chocolate sponge cake	朱古力蛋糕 1 片
Ganache	**朱古力醬**
100 g chocolate	朱古力 100 克
50 g whipped cream	鮮忌廉 50 克
10 g butter	牛油 10 克

1. Add gelatine to water in a bowl over simmering water.
2. Heat sugar until caramelized. Add 100 g whipping cream and coconut milk. Cook briefly.
3. Add dissolved gelatine and mix well. Pour in instant coffee powder. Mix well.
4. Beat egg yolks in a bowl over simmering water. Keep stirring until smooth. Remove from heat. Add the mixture from (3). Mix well.
5. Add 200 g whipping cream and combine.
6. Line the bottom of a cake tin with sponge cake. Pour in mousse. Refrigerate for 4 hours. Serve with ganache.

Ganache

Finely chop chocolate. Add whipping cream and butter. Heat until butter melts. Strain and leave it to cool.

1. 將明膠粉和水調勻,隔熱水溶化。
2. 將糖煮成焦糖,加入100克鮮忌廉和椰漿煮成焦糖漿。
3. 加入溶化明膠粉,拌勻;下即溶咖啡粉,拌勻。
4. 隔熱水打發蛋黃至光滑,離火,加入(3),拌勻。
5. 打發200克鮮忌廉,加入混合物內拌勻。
6. 慕思模底部墊蛋糕,倒入慕思,放入冰箱冷凍4小時即可,可伴朱古力醬享用。

朱古力醬

將朱古力切碎,加入鮮忌廉和牛油一起隔熱水溶化,過濾,待涼即可。

Milk Tea Coffee Pudding

鴛鴦奶茶咖啡布丁

Coffee Pudding
600 ml milk
80 g whipping cream
60 g sugar
20 g instant jelly powder
60 ml water
10 g instant coffee powder

Tea Pudding
2 tea bags
800 ml milk
200 g sugar
20 g instant jelly powder

咖啡布丁
牛奶 600 毫升
鮮忌廉 80 克
糖 60 克
果凍粉 20 克
水 60 毫升
即溶咖啡粉 10 克

茶布丁
紅茶包 2 包
牛奶 800 毫升
糖 200 克
果凍粉 20 克

Method 做法

Coffee Pudding

1. Dissolve instant coffee powder in water.
2. Mix instant jelly powder and sugar. Pour in milk. Bring to the boil. Add whipping cream and coffee from step (1). Bring to the boil again. Remove from heat.

Tea Pudding

1. Heat milk up to 80°C. Remove from heat. Soak tea bags in milk for 10 minutes.
2. Combine sugar and instant jelly powder. Pour in milk. Heat up to 80°C. Remove from heat.

To Assemble

Spoon coffee pudding into a pudding mould. Refrigerate until coffee pudding is almost set. Pour in tea pudding.

咖啡布丁

1. 用水調勻即溶咖啡粉。
2. 果凍粉和糖拌勻,加入牛奶,煮滾,加入鮮忌廉、咖啡水再煮滾,離火。

茶布丁

1. 將牛奶加熱至 80℃,離火,放入紅茶包浸泡 10 分鐘。
2. 將糖和果凍粉拌勻,加入牛奶,加熱至80℃,離火。

綜合做法

先將咖啡布丁倒入模內,接近凝固時,再倒入茶布丁。

Coconut Pudding

椰纖果果凍

10 g konnyaku powder
100 g sugar
400 ml coconut juice
600 ml water
young coconut flesh
nata de coco

水晶果凍粉 10 克
糖 100 克
椰子水 400 毫升
水 600 毫升
嫩椰子肉適量
椰纖果肉適量

Method 做法

1. Pour out coconut juice from young coconut. Spoon out coconut flesh.
2. Mix sugar and konnyaku powder. Add water and bring to the boil over medium heat. Pour in coconut juice and bring to the boil.
3. Remove from heat. Add coconut flesh and nata de coco.
4. Spoon in jelly moulds. Set aside. Refrigerate until jelly is set.

1. 將嫩椰子內的椰子水倒出，用湯匙刮出椰子肉。
2. 拌勻糖和果凍粉，加入水，用中火煮滾，下椰子水，繼續加熱至滾。
3. 離火，加入椰子肉和椰纖果肉。
4. 將混合料倒入果凍模內，待涼，放入冰箱待凝固。

Water Chestnut Agar-agar with Yam
山藥馬蹄果凍

Ingredients 材料

Ingredients 材料	
300 g yam	山藥（鮮淮山）300 克
1 tbsp Gou Qi Zi	枸杞子 1 湯匙
10 water chestnuts	馬蹄 10 粒
10 g agar-agar powder	燕菜粉 10 克
100 g sugar	糖 100 克
1 litre water	水 1 公升

Method 做法

1. Mash yam using a tablespoon.
2. Peel water chestnuts and chop finely.
3. Soak Gou Qi Zi in water and drain.
4. Mix agar-agar powder with sugar. Add water and bring to the boil over medium heat. Reduce to low heat and simmer for 5 minutes.
5. Remove from heat. Put in yam, Gou Qi Zi and water chestnuts. Mix well. Spoon into jelly cups. Set aside. Refrigerate until set. Serve.

1. 山藥用湯匙搗成泥狀。
2. 馬蹄去皮、切碎。
3. 將枸杞子浸泡，濾乾水分。
4. 燕菜粉加糖拌勻，加入水，用中火煮滾，轉調小火再煮 5 分鐘。
5. 離火，加入山藥、枸杞子和馬蹄拌勻，倒入模子內待涼，放入冰箱待凝固。

Durian Mousse

榴槤芝士慕思

300 g durian puree
50 g sugar
3 egg yolks
150 g whipping cream
150 g non-dairy
whipped topping
12 g gelatine
60 ml warm water
100 ml milk
100 g cream cheese
1 slice sponge cake

榴槤果肉 300 克
糖 50 克
蛋黃 3 個
鮮忌廉 150 克
植物性鮮忌廉 150 克
明膠粉 12 克
溫水 60 毫升
牛奶 100 毫升
忌廉芝士 100 克
海綿蛋糕 1 片

Method | 做法

1. Dissolve gelatine in warm water.
2. Beat cream cheese and sugar until smooth. Add egg yolks and mix well. Heat until sugar dissolves.
3. Add dissolved gelatine. Pour in milk and durian puree. Mix well. Leave it to cool.
4. In a separate bowl, beat whipping cream and non-dairy whipped topping until fluffy. Add the cream mixture to the durian mixture. Fold in well.
5. Fill cup with mousse until 1/3 full. Put in 1 piece of cake. Pour in mousse again to fill the cup completely.
6. Refrigerate for 4 hours. Serve.

1. 將明膠粉加溫水調勻至溶化。
2. 忌廉芝士加糖攪拌至光滑，加入蛋黃拌勻，隔水加熱至糖溶解。
3. 加入已溶化的明膠粉，再下牛奶和榴槤果肉拌勻，待涼。
4. 一起打發兩種鮮忌廉，加入混合料內成慕思。
5. 慕思舀進杯內約 1/3 杯滿，再放入一片蛋糕，再倒入慕思。其餘慕思均如法炮製。
6. 慕思放入冰箱冷凍 4 小時即可食用。

Black Glutinous Rice Pudding
香蕉紫米布丁

100 g cooked black
glutinous rice
3 bananas (mashed)
120 ml milk
40 g whipping cream
30 g sugar
2 eggs

紫米（黑糯米）飯 100 克
香蕉（搗爛）3 條
牛奶 120 毫升
鮮忌廉 40 克
糖 30 克
蛋 2 個

1. Heat milk, whipping cream and sugar together until sugar dissolves.
2. Whisk eggs gently. Add all the other ingredients and mix well.
3. Spoon mixture into mould. Steam over low heat for 30 minutes or until done. Serve.

1. 將牛奶、鮮忌廉和糖一起煮至糖溶解。
2. 蛋輕輕攪勻，加入所有材料，拌勻。
3. 將混合料倒入模子內，用小火蒸 30 分鐘或至熟即可。

Sesame Peanut Pudding
芝麻花生布丁

Black Sesame Pudding
100 g black sesames
300 ml milk
50 g whipping cream
5 g agar-agar powder
60 g sugar
150 ml water

Peanut Pudding
100 g peanut butter
20 g sugar
6 g agar agar powder
300 ml water
200 ml milk

黑芝麻布丁
黑芝麻 100 克
牛奶 300 毫升
鮮忌廉 50 克
燕菜粉 5 克
糖 60 克
水 150 毫升

花生布丁
花生醬 100 克
糖 20 克
燕菜粉 6 克
水 300 毫升
牛奶 200 毫升

Method 做法

Black Sesame Pudding

1. Stir fry black sesames in a dry wok until fragrant. Grind finely.
2. Mix sugar with agar-agar powder. Pour in water, ground black sesames, milk and whipping cream. Bring to the boil over medium heat.

Peanut Pudding

Mix agar-agar powder and sugar. Pour in water, milk and peanut butter. Bring to the boil over medium heat.

To Assemble

Spoon a thin layer of black sesame pudding into pudding tin. Leave it until set. Score the surface gently with a knife. Pour in peanut pudding. Repeat the step with sesame and peanut pudding alternately.

黑芝麻布丁

1. 用白鑊將黑芝麻炒香,用磨碎機磨成芝麻粉。
2. 燕菜粉加糖拌勻,加入水、黑芝麻粉、牛奶和鮮忌廉,用中火煮滾即可。

花生布丁

將燕菜粉和糖拌勻,加入水、牛奶和花生醬,用中火煮滾即可。

綜合做法

將一層黑芝麻布丁倒入模子內,待凝固,用刀子在布丁表面稍微刮線條,再倒一層花生布丁,重複這步驟,布丁即呈美麗的一層層花紋。

Yogurt Pudding
乳酪布丁

Yogurt Jelly	乳酪果凍層
400 g yogurt	乳酪 400 克
10 g konnyaku jelly powder	水晶果凍粉 10 克
100 g sugar	糖 100 克
600 ml water	水 600 毫升
Fruit Jelly	**水果果凍層**
5 g konnyaku jelly powder	水晶果凍粉 5 克
50 g sugar	糖 50 克
500 ml water	水 500 毫升
5 strawberries (diced)	草莓 5 粒（切粒）
1 kiwifruit (diced)	奇異果 1 個（切粒）

Method 做法

Yogurt Jelly

1. Combine sugar and konnyaku jelly powder.
2. Add water and bring to the boil over high heat. Reduce to low heat and simmer for 5 minutes.
3. Pour in yogurt. Bring to the boil. Remove from heat.
4. Spoon the mixture into champagne glass until half full. Leave it to set.

Fruit Jelly

1. Combine sugar and konnyaku jelly powder. Add water and bring to the boil over high heat.
2. Pour the mixture over the yogurt jelly. Put diced strawberry and kiwifruit on top of yogurt pudding. Serve.

乳酪果凍層

1. 將糖和果凍粉調勻。
2. 加入水，用大火煮至滾，轉調小火繼續煮5分鐘，關火。
3. 加入乳酪煮至滾，關火。
4. 將混合物倒入香檳杯內，大約半杯即可，待凝固。

水果果凍層

1. 將糖和果凍粉調勻，加入水，用大火煮至沸，轉調小火繼續煮 5 分鐘，即可關火。
2. 將混合物倒在乳酪果凍層上，再放入已切小塊的草莓和奇異果即可。

Longan Sorbet
龍眼冰沙

300 g shelled longans
50 ml water
50 g sugar
100 g whipping cream
100 ml milk
1 slice cantaloup

龍眼果肉 300 克
水 50 毫升
糖 50 克
鮮忌廉 100 克
牛奶 100 毫升
哈密瓜 1 塊

Method 做法

1. Heat sugar in water over medium heat until sugar dissolves.
2. Blend cantaloup and longans into puree.
3. Beat whipping cream until fluffy.
4. Stir all the ingredients together. Pour into a tray. Refrigerate for 4 hours. Use spoon to scrape the ice and serve immediately.

1. 將糖和水一起用中火煮,待糖煮溶。
2. 將龍眼果肉和哈密瓜一起磨成泥。
3. 打發鮮忌廉。
4. 將所有材料一起拌勻,倒入盤子內,放入冰箱冷凍 4 小時,然後用湯匙刮出成碎冰即可食用。

CHEESECAKE

芝 士 蛋 糕

Not only are they low in
sugar and fat,
making these cheesecakes
is also as easy as ABC.
And you don't worry about
gaining weight too!

低糖、低脂又製作簡易的
芝士蛋糕，
讓大家做得開心、吃得放心！

Lemon Cheesecake

檸檬芝士蛋糕

Ingredients 材料

150 g ricotta cheese	低脂芝士 150 克
20 g sugar	糖 20 克
1 egg yolk	蛋黃 1 個
35 ml milk	牛奶 35 毫升
5 g gelatine	明膠粉 5 克
50 ml warm water	溫水 50 毫升
100 g whipping cream	鮮忌廉 100 克
1 lemon (juiced)	檸檬（榨汁）1 個
1 lemon zest (grated)	檸檬皮（磨茸）1 個
1 slice sponge cake	海綿蛋糕 1 片
Garnish	**裝飾**
100 g non-dairy whipped topping	植物性鮮忌廉 100 克
50 g croquent	玉米粒 50 克
instant jelly glaze	亮面果膠（適量）

Method 做法

1. Dissolve gelatine in warm water.
2. Beat cheese, egg and sugar until smooth.
3. Add dissolved gelatine. Pour in milk and combine. In a separate bowl, beat whipping cream until fluffy. Add cream to the cheese mixture.
4. Add lemon zest and lemon juice. Stir gently.
5. Line the bottom of a cake tin with sponge cake. Spread the cheese mixture over sponge cake. Refrigerate for 4 hours.

Garnish

1. Spread the instant jelly glaze onto the surface of the cake.
2. Coat the sides in whipped topping first and then croquent.

1. 將明膠粉加溫水調勻至溶化。
2. 芝士、糖和蛋攪拌至光滑。
3. 加入已溶化的明膠粉，下牛奶拌勻，再加入已打發的鮮忌廉。
4. 下檸檬皮茸和檸檬汁輕輕拌勻即可。
5. 將蛋糕餡倒入已墊海綿蛋糕的模子內，放入冰箱冷凍 4 小時即可享用。

裝飾

1. 在蛋糕面塗上亮面果膠。
2. 旁邊塗上已打發的鮮忌廉，再用玉米粒裝飾即可。

Tiramisu
意大利芝士蛋糕

Ingredients 材料

Chocolate Cake
4 egg yolks, 110 g sugar,
100 g superfine flour,
20 g cocoa powder, 4 egg whites,
40 g melted butter

Mousse
3 egg yolks, 20 g sugar,
250 g mascarpone cheese,
150 g whipping cream, Tia Maria

Coffee Syrup
1 cup Espresso coffee, 1 tbsp sugar,
1 tbsp Tia Maria

Garnish
cocoa powder

朱古力蛋糕
蛋黃 4 個，糖 110 克，低筋麵粉 100
克，可可粉 20 克，蛋白 4 個，
溶化牛油 40 克

慕思
蛋黃 3 個，糖 20 克，馬士卡邦芝士
250 克，鮮忌廉 150 克，
咖啡酒隨意

咖啡糖漿
濃縮咖啡 1 杯，糖 1 湯匙，
咖啡酒 1 湯匙

裝飾
可可粉適量

Chocolate Cake

1. Beat egg yolks and 50 g sugar until pale.
2. Beat egg whites and 60 g sugar until soft peaks form.
3. Sift superfine flour and cocoa powder together.
4. Pour half the egg white mixture into egg yolk mixture. Stir gently.
5. Fold in sifted superfine flour and cocoa flour. Fold in the remaining egg white mixture. Add butter. Mix well.
6. Pour the mixture into cake tin. Bake at 180°C for 30 minutes. Remove cake from the oven and set aside to cool. Cut the cake into pieces.

Mousse

1. Put egg yolks and sugar into a bowl over simmering water. Beat until pale.
2. Add mascarpone cheese and combine. Add whipped fresh cream.
3. Add Tia Maria and mix well.

Coffee Syrup

Bring espresso coffee and sugar to the boil. Pour in Tia Maria. Mix well.

To Assemble

Pour 1/3 cup of mousse into mould. Soak a slice of chocolate cake in coffee syrup. Put it over the mousse. Pour 1/3 cup of mousse on top. Repeat the process until all the mousse and cake is used up. Chill for 4 hours. Dust cocoa powder on top. Serve.

朱古力蛋糕

1. 將蛋黃和 50 克糖打至變白成蛋黃糊。
2. 將蛋白和 60 克糖打至濕性發泡。
3. 低筋麵粉和可可粉一起篩勻。
4. 將一半蛋白加入蛋黃糊內，輕輕拌勻。
5. 加入已篩的低筋麵粉和可可粉，最後加入剩餘的蛋白拌勻，加入牛油，拌勻。
6. 倒入烤模，以 180℃ 烘焙 30 分鐘。將蛋糕移離烤爐，待凍後切件。

慕思

1. 將蛋黃和糖隔熱水打至變白。
2. 加入芝士拌勻，捲入已打發的鮮忌廉。
3. 下咖啡酒拌勻即成。

咖啡糖漿

將咖啡和糖一起煮溶，加入咖啡酒，拌勻。

綜合做法

先倒 1/3 杯慕思入模子內，再放一片已浸泡咖啡糖漿的朱古力蛋糕，再倒入慕思覆蓋蛋糕，重複這做法一次。將意大利芝士蛋糕放入冰箱冷藏 4 小時，在表面撒上可可粉即成。

Herb and Cheese Scone
香料芝士鬆餅

250 g flour	麵粉 250 克
1 tsp baking powder	發粉 1 茶匙
80 g unsalted butter	無鹽牛油 80 克
100 g Cheddar cheese	車打芝士 100 克
1 tsp oregano	奧勒根 1 茶匙
1 tsp thyme	百里香 1 茶匙
1 tsp rosemary	迷迭香 1 茶匙
150 ml milk	牛奶 150 毫升

Method 做法

1. Sift flour and baking powder together. Set aside.
2. Beat butter until soft. Add all the other ingredients. Mix together to make dough.
3. Roll the dough out to 1 cm thick. Use a heart-shaped cutter to cut out scones. Place scones into a greased baking tray. Bake for 15-20 minutes or till golden brown. Serve with jam or butter.

1. 將麵粉和發粉篩勻，備用。
2. 將牛油拌軟，加入所有材料一起拌成麵糰即可。
3. 將麵糰擀成1吋厚，用心形切模切開麵糰，然後放在已塗油的烤盤內，烘焙15-20分鐘或至金黃色即可。可用果醬或牛油伴食。

Low Fat Cheesecake
低脂乳酪芝士蛋糕

Ingredients 材料

100 g digestive biscuits	消化餅乾 100 克
50 g melted butter	溶化牛油 50 克
200 g cream cheese	忌廉芝士 200 克
20 g sugar	糖 20 克
80 g sour cream	酸忌廉 80 克
70 g yogurt	乳酪 70 克
50 g whipping cream	鮮忌廉 50 克
40 g egg white	蛋白 40 克
20 g sugar	糖 20 克

Method 做法

1. Crush biscuits. Mix biscuits with melted butter. Press the mixture onto the bottom of a cake tin.
2. Beat cream cheese and sugar until fluffy. Pour in sour cream and yogurt. Mix well. Fold in whipping cream.
3. Beat egg white and sugar at medium speed until soft peaks form. Pour in cheese mixture and mix well.
4. Pour the mixture into cake tin over the biscuit base. Bake in water bath at 150°C for 50-60 minutes.

1. 壓碎餅乾，和溶化牛油混合，然後壓在烤模底部。
2. 將忌廉芝士和糖打發，加入酸忌廉、乳酪，拌勻。加入鮮忌廉，拌勻。
3. 蛋白和糖用中速攪拌至濕性發泡，加入芝士糊內拌勻。
4. 倒入烤模內，以 150℃隔水烘焙 50-60 分鐘。

Light Cinnamon Cheesecake

輕軟肉桂芝士蛋糕

60 ml milk	牛奶 60 毫升
120 g cream cheese	忌廉芝士 120 克
30 g butter	牛油 30 克
20 g superfine flour	低筋麵粉 20 克
20 g cornflour	粟粉 20 克
4 eggs yolks	蛋黃 4 個
10 g ground cinnamon	肉桂粉 10 克
4 egg whites	蛋白 4 個
50 g sugar	糖 50 克
1/4 tsp salt	鹽 1/4 茶匙

Method 做法

1. Heat butter, milk and cream cheese in a metal bowl over a hot water bath. Whisk until lump-free.

2. Add egg yolks and combine.

3. Stir in sifted superfine flour, cornflour and cinnamon.

4. In a separate bowl, beat egg whites until foamy. Add sugar and salt. Keep beating at medium speed until soft peaks form.

5. Fold half of the egg white mixture into the egg yolk mixture. Stir gently. Fold in the rest of the egg white mixture.

6. Pour the mixture into a greased cake tin lined with baking paper. Bake in water bath at 150°C for 50 minutes.

1. 牛油、牛奶和忌廉芝士一起隔熱水加熱，用打蛋器拌至光滑沒有顆粒。

2. 加入蛋黃拌勻。

3. 下已篩勻的低筋麵粉、粟粉和肉桂粉，拌勻。

4. 蛋白打發至起泡，加入糖和鹽繼續以中速打至濕性發泡。

5. 將已打發的蛋白分兩次加入麵糊內，輕輕拌勻。

6. 倒入已塗油墊紙的烤模內，以150℃隔水烘焙50分鐘即可。

Chocolate Mint Cheesecake
薄荷芝士蛋糕

Chocolate Cake	朱古力蛋糕
3 egg yolks	蛋黃 3 個
60 g sugar	糖 60 克
3 egg whites	蛋白 3 個
60 g superfine flour	低筋麵粉 60 克
20 g cocoa powder	可可粉 20 克
40 g melted butter	溶化牛油 40 克
20 ml milk	牛奶 20 毫升
Mint Cheesecake	**薄荷芝士蛋糕**
250 g cream cheese	忌廉芝士 250 克
40 g sugar	糖 40 克
3 eggs	蛋 3 個
50 g fresh cream	鮮忌廉 50 克
1 tbsp peppermint essence	薄荷香精 1 湯匙

Method 做法

Chocolate Cake

1. Beat egg yolks and 30 g sugar until fluffy. Stir in superfine flour, cocoa powder, milk and melted butter.
2. Beat egg whites and sugar until soft peaks form. Fold egg whites into the egg yolk mixture.
3. Pour the mixture into cake tin. Bake at 180°C for 25 minutes or until done.

To Assemble

1. Combine cream cheese and sugar.
2. Add one egg at a time. Beating well after each addition.
3. Fold in whipping cream and peppermint essence.
4. Lined the bottom of a cake tin with chocolate cake. Pour the cream cheese batter into the cake tin over the cake base. Bake in water bath at 160°C for 50 minutes.

朱古力蛋糕

1. 將蛋黃和 30 克糖打發，加入低筋麵粉、可可粉、牛奶和溶化牛油，拌勻。
2. 將蛋白和 30 克糖打發至濕性發泡，蛋白加入麵糊內拌勻。
3. 麵糊倒進烤模內，以 180℃烘焙 25 分鐘至熟即可。

綜合做法

1. 將忌廉芝士加糖拌勻。
2. 蛋分次加入，拌勻。
3. 最後加入鮮忌廉和薄荷香精攪拌均勻即可。
4. 倒入已墊朱古力蛋糕的烤模內，以160℃隔水烘焙 50 分鐘即成。

Supreme Chocolate Cheesecake
朱古力芝士蛋糕

1 slice chocolate cake	朱古力蛋糕 1 片
300 g cream cheese	忌廉芝士 300 克
50 g sugar	糖 50 克
3 egg yolks	蛋黃 3 個
50 g sour cream	酸忌廉 50 克
20 g cornflour	粟粉 20 克
100 g cooking chocolate	煮食朱古力 100 克
(chopped)	（切碎）
3 egg whites	蛋白 3 個
30 g sugar	糖 30 克

Method 做法

1. Heat the chopped chocolate in a double-boiler or over a water bath. Stir until chocolate melts. Set aside.
2. Beat cream cheese and sugar until lump-free. Fold in sour cream, egg yolks, cornflour and melted chocolate.
3. Beat egg whites and sugar at medium speed until soft peaks form. Add the egg white mixture to the cream cheese mixture a little at a time. Stir gently after each addition.
4. Line the bottom of a cake tin with chocolate cake. Pour the cream cheese batter into the cake tin over the cake base. Bake in a water bath at 150°C for 50 - 60 minutes.

1. 隔熱水攪煮朱古力至溶化，待用。
2. 將忌廉芝士和糖攪拌至沒有顆粒，加入酸忌廉、蛋黃、粟粉和溶化朱古力，拌勻。
3. 蛋白和糖用中速打發至濕性發泡，分次加入芝士麵糊內，輕輕拌勻。
4. 將朱古力蛋糕放入烤模內，再倒下芝士混合料，以 150℃ 隔水烘焙 50-60 分鐘。

Raspberry Cheese Roll

覆盆子芝士卷

(A)	**(A)**
20 g cocoa powder	可可粉 20 克
50 ml water	水 50 毫升
(B)	**(B)**
70 g superfine flour	低筋麵粉 70 克
1/6 tsp baking powder	發粉 1/6 茶匙
20 g sugar	糖 20 克
1/4 tsp salt	鹽 1/4 茶匙
(C)	**(C)**
30 g cooking oil	食油 30 克
4 egg yolks	蛋黃 4 個
30 ml milk	牛奶 30 毫升
(D)	**(D)**
4 egg whites	蛋白 4 個
50 g sugar	糖 50 克
1/2 tsp cream of tartar	塔塔粉 1/2 茶匙
Filling	**餡料**
150 g ricotta cheese	低脂芝士 150 克
100 g raspberry jam	覆盆子果醬 100 克
Garnish	**裝飾**
raspberries	覆盆子適量
chocolate leaf	朱古力葉片
sliced green apple	青蘋果
lemon zest	檸檬皮

Method 做法

1. Stir cocoa powder in water until well incorporated.
2. Combine superfine flour, baking powder, sugar and salt. Pour in oil, egg yolks, milk and dissolved cocoa powder. Combine.
3. Beat egg whites, sugar and cream of tartar until soft peaks form. Fold half of the egg white into the flour mixture. Stir gently. Fold in the rest of egg white.
4. Pour into 12 x 12" baking tray lined with baking paper. Flatten the surface.
5. Bake at 180°C for 15 minutes.

To Assemble

1. Spread ricotta cheese over the cake. Cover with raspberry jam. Roll it up like Swiss roll (For the making method of Swiss roll, please refer to P.27). Refrigerate for 30 minutes.
2. Cut into slices of 1 1/2 inch thick. Spread cheese on the surface. Garnish and serve.

1. 將可可粉和水一起攪拌至沒有顆粒。
2. 將低筋麵粉、發粉、糖和鹽拌勻，加入食油、蛋黃、牛奶和溶化的可可粉一起攪拌均勻。
3. 蛋白、糖和塔塔粉一起打發至濕性發泡，分兩次加入麵糊內，輕輕拌勻。
4. 倒入已墊紙的 12×12 吋烤盤內，抹平。
5. 以 180℃ 烤焙 15 分鐘即可。

綜合做法

1. 在蛋糕表面塗上一層芝士，再塗上一層覆盆子果醬，捲起成瑞士卷（瑞士卷製法可參考第 27 頁的椰香班蘭卷），放入冰箱冷藏 30 分鐘。
2. 將瑞士卷切成 1 1/2 吋的寬度，表面塗一層芝士，再放上裝飾即可。

PIE•TART•PUFF

■

派 • 塔 • 泡芙

With crispy crust and
yummy filling,
these goodies
will surely bring you
a new taste sensation.

多款酥脆、
透着誘人甜香的美食，
保證能為你的味覺
帶來新刺激！

Linzer Torte
林芝塔

200 g butter, 120 g icing sugar	牛油 200 克，糖粉 120 克
2 eggs, 1 egg yolk	蛋 2 個，蛋黃 1 個
1 tsp grated lemon zest	檸檬皮茸 1 茶匙
1/2 tsp ground clove	丁香粉 1/2 茶匙
1/2 tsp ground cinnamon	肉桂粉 1/2 茶匙
30 g ground hazelnut	榛子粉 30 克
30 g ground walnut	核桃粉 30 克
30 g ground almond	杏仁粉 30 克
120 g superfine flour	低筋麵粉 120 克
1/4 tsp baking powder	發粉 1/4 茶匙
50 g cake crumbs	蛋糕屑 50 克
150 g raspberry jam	覆盆子果醬 150 克

Method 做法

1. Cream butter and icing sugar until fluffy. Stir in egg yolk.
2. Add one egg at a time. Beat well after each addition.
3. Put in lemon zest, ground cinnamon, ground clove, ground hazelnut, ground walnut and ground almond. Mix well.
4. Fold in sifted flour, baking powder and cake crumbs. Mix well.
5. Line the bottom of a 8-inch tart tin with baking paper and grease the sides. Put the batter into a piping bag with nozzle. Pipe a layer of the egg mixture onto the bottom of tart tin. Also pipe onto the sides (as shown in 1).
6. Spread raspberry jam over the mixture (as shown in 2). Pipe narrow strips of batter on top. Interweave them to make a lattice top for the tart (as shown in 3).
7. Bake at 180°C for 40 minutes or until done. Serve.

1. 牛油和糖粉一起打發，加入蛋黃拌勻。
2. 蛋分次加入，攪拌均勻。
3. 加入檸檬皮茸、肉桂粉、丁香粉、榛子粉、核桃粉和杏仁粉，拌勻。
4. 加入已篩的低筋麵粉、發粉和蛋糕屑，拌勻。
5. 8吋塔模底部墊紙、塔模邊塗油。將麵糊盛入擠花袋內，在塔模內擠一層麵糊，再在邊緣擠一圈（看圖 1）。
6. 塗上覆盆子果醬（看圖 2），再擠上麵糊呈格子狀（看圖 3）。
7. 以 180℃ 烘烤 40 分鐘至熟即可。

1.

2.

3.

Pumpkin Tarts
南瓜塔

Tart Pastry
80 g butter
40 g icing sugar
1/4 tsp salt
1 egg
1/2 tsp vanilla essence
200 g flour
10 g milk powder

Filling
30 g sugar
400 g pumpkin
50 g ground almond
1 egg
50 g almond flakes

塔皮
牛油 80 克
糖粉 40 克
鹽 1/4 茶匙
蛋 1 個
雲尼拿香精 1/2 茶匙
麵粉 200 克
奶粉 10 克

餡料
糖 30 克
南瓜 400 克
杏仁粉 50 克
蛋 1 個
杏仁片 50 克

Method 做法

Tart Pastry
1. Cream butter until soft. Add sifted icing sugar and salt. Beat until fluffy.
2. Add egg and vanilla essence. Keep stirring.
3. Sift flour and milk powder onto the worktop. Add butter mixture. Knead into soft dough. Set aside for 30 minutes.
4. Press a small piece of dough into each greased tart tin. Trim the edges with a spatula. Bake at 180°C for 10 minutes.

Pumpkin Filling
1. Peel and seed pumpkin. Cut into small pieces and steam until done. Mash.
2. Combine sugar, egg and ground almond. Spoon the filling into baked tart pastry.
3. Garnish with almond flakes. Bake at 180°C for 15-20 minutes. Serve.

塔皮
1. 打軟牛油，加入已篩的糖粉和鹽，再一起打發。
2. 加入蛋和香精繼續攪拌均勻。
3. 將麵粉和奶粉一起篩在工作枱上，倒入已打發的牛油混合物，用手壓成軟麵糰；然後讓麵糰鬆弛 30 分鐘。
4. 取一小塊麵糰壓入已塗油的塔模內，用刮刀去掉多餘的麵糰，以180℃烘焙 10 分鐘。

南瓜餡
1. 將南瓜去皮、去籽、切小塊，蒸熟，壓成南瓜泥。
2. 加入糖、蛋和杏仁粉拌勻，將餡料倒進已烤熟的塔皮內。
3. 撒上杏仁片裝飾，以 180℃ 烤 15-20 分鐘即可。

Almond Fruit Tarts
水果杏仁塔

Tart Pastry

80 g butter

40 g icing sugar

1/4 tsp salt

1 egg

1/2 tsp vanilla essence

200 g flour

10 g milk powder

Filling

50 g instant custard powder

130 ml water

100 g whipped cream

Almond Cake

120 g butter

50 g icing sugar

2 eggs

50 g ground almond

80 g superfine flour

1/4 tsp baking powder

Garnish

fruits

塔皮

牛油 80 克

糖粉 40 克

鹽 1/4 茶匙

蛋 1 個

雲尼拿香精 1/2 茶匙

麵粉 200 克

奶粉 10 克

餡料

即食蛋黃粉 50 克

水 130 毫升

打發鮮忌廉 100 克

杏仁蛋糕

牛油 120 克

糖粉 50 克

蛋 2 個

杏仁粉 50 克

低筋麵粉 80 克

發粉 1/4 茶匙

裝飾

水果適量

Tart Pastry

1. Cream butter until soft. Add sifted icing sugar and salt. Beat until fluffy.
2. Add egg and vanilla essence. Stir well.
3. Sift flour and milk powder onto the worktop. Pour in beaten butter. Knead into soft dough. Set aside for 30 minutes.
4. Press a small piece of dough into each tart tin. Trim the edges with a spatula.

Filling

Mix instant custard powder with water. Fold in whipped cream.

Almond Cake

1. Cream butter until soft. Add icing sugar and stir until fluffy.
2. Add one egg at a time. Beat well after each addition.
3. Put in ground almond, superfine flour and baking powder. Spoon into tart pastry. Bake at 180°C for 20 minutes.
4. Leave it to cool. Pipe filling on tart. Garnish with fruits.

塔皮

1. 將牛油打軟,加入已篩的糖粉和鹽,打發。
2. 加入蛋和雲尼拿香精繼續攪拌均勻。
3. 將麵粉和奶粉篩在工作枱上,倒入已打發的牛油,用手壓成軟麵糰,再讓麵糰鬆弛30分鐘。
4. 取一小塊麵糰壓入已塗油的塔模內,用刮刀去掉多餘的麵糰。

餡料

將即食蛋黃粉加水拌勻,下已打發的鮮忌廉拌勻。

杏仁蛋糕

1. 將牛油打軟,加入糖粉攪拌至鬆發。
2. 分次加入蛋,攪拌至光滑。
3. 加入杏仁粉、低筋麵粉和發粉,然後倒入塔皮內,以180℃烘烤20分鐘。
4. 待杏仁塔冷卻後,擠上餡料,再以水果裝飾即成。

Napoleon

拿破崙派

Ingredients 材料

Pie Pastry

250 g flour

150 ml water

1/2 tsp salt

10 g sugar

120 g pastry margarine

Egg White Frosting

4 egg whites

50 g sugar

30 g raisins

French Custard

250 ml milk

12 g cornflour

12 g superfine flour

50 g sugar

2 egg yolks

10 g butter

100 g whipping cream, whipped

派皮

麵粉 250 克

水 150 毫升

鹽 1/2 茶匙

糖 10 克

起酥油 120 克

蛋白霜

蛋白 4 個

糖 50 克

葡萄乾 30 克

法式蛋黃醬

牛奶 250 毫升

粟粉 12 克

低筋麵粉 12 克

糖 50 克

蛋黃 2 個

牛油 10 克

鮮忌廉 100 克（打發）

1.

2.

3.

4.

5.

6.

pie>>tart>>puff

Pie Pastry

1. Dissolve salt and sugar in water. Cut pastry margarine into 1 inch cube. Add flour and mix well.
2. Pour in water and stir gently until the flour absorbs the water and turns into a rough dough (as shown in 1).
3. Knead the mixture to make dough. Pound gently with a rolling pin (as shown in 2). Set aside for 20 minutes.
4. Roll out the dough into a long sheet, about 3 mm thick (as shown in 3).
5. Fold the dough into thirds by bringing in the sides (as shown in 4). Pound gently with a rolling pin (as shown in 5). Roll it out again with a rolling pin (as shown in 6). Roll out the dough into a 3-mm thickness. Repeat this step three times (as shown in 4-6). Leave the dough to rest for 30 minutes.
6. Roll out the dough into a long sheet, about 3 mm thick. Cut into 4 x 3 inch rectangles. Prick the surface with a fork. Brush egg yolk over it. Bake at 200°C until golden brown.

Egg White Frosting

1. Beat egg whites until light and fluffy. Add half of the sugar at a time, beating well after each addition. Add raisins and mix well.
2. Spoon the mixture into 12 x 12 inch baking tray. Spread evenly. Bake at 180°C for 10-20 minutes. Cut into 4 x 3 inch rectangles.

French Custard

1. Heat milk up to 80°C.
2. Beat sugar and egg yolks until pale. Pour in hot milk and mix well. Add cornflour and superfine flour. Heat together until thick. Remove from heat.
3. Fold in butter. Leave it to cool. Add whipped cream to the flour mixture. Stir well.

To Assemble

1. Spread custard onto one of the baked pastry. Put the egg white frosting over it.
2. Top with second piece of baked pastry and repeat step (1). Top with third piece of pastry. Dust icing sugar on top.

派皮

1. 用水將鹽和糖拌溶。將起酥油切成1吋方塊，倒入麵粉，拌勻。
2. 倒入水，稍微拌勻至水分被麵粉吸收成粗糙粉糰（看圖1）。
3. 用手將粗糙麵糰壓成麵糰，再用擀麵棒略搥（看圖2），然後讓麵糰鬆弛20分鐘。
4. 將麵糰擀成長形，大約3毫米厚（看圖3）。
5. 摺成3折（看圖4），用擀麵棒略搥（看圖5），再擀開（看圖6）。重複3次，做法請看圖4-6，然後讓麵糰鬆弛30分鐘。
6. 將麵糰擀成3毫米厚的長形，再切成4吋×3吋的長形。用叉子在麵皮上戳洞，塗上蛋黃，以200℃烤至金黃色即可。

蛋白霜

1. 將蛋白打至起泡，糖分2次加入，打發至乾性發泡，加入葡萄乾拌勻。
2. 將蛋白倒入12吋×12吋的烤盤內，抹平。以180℃烘焙10-20分鐘即可，切成4吋×3吋的長形。

法式蛋黃醬

1. 將牛奶加熱至80℃。
2. 糖和蛋黃一起攪拌至變白，加入熱牛奶，拌勻。下粟粉和低筋麵粉，一起加熱至濃稠，離火。
3. 加入牛油拌勻，待涼，加入已打發的鮮忌廉，拌勻成蛋黃醬。

綜合做法

1. 一片派皮上塗少許蛋黃醬，放上蛋白霜。
2. 蓋上另一片派皮，塗上蛋黃醬和放上蛋白霜，蓋上第三片派皮，灑上糖霜即成。

Mango Pie
芒果派

Pie Pastry

400 g flour, 180 g shortening, 1/4 tsp salt, 10 g sugar, 140 ml water

Mango Custard

200 g milk, 50 g sugar, 10 g superfine flour, 10 g cornflour, 2 egg yolks, 100 g mango puree, 20 g butter

Garnish

mango and pomegranate

派皮

麵粉 400 克，白油 180 克，鹽 1/4 茶匙，糖 10 克，水 140 毫升

芒果蛋黃醬

牛奶 200 克，糖 50 克，低筋麵粉 10 克，粟粉 10 克，蛋黃 2 個，芒果泥 100 克，牛油 20 克

裝飾

芒果及石榴子適量

Method 做法

Pie Pastry

1. Dissolve sugar and salt in water.
2. Sift flour. Put in shortening. Cut shortening into 1/2-inch cubes.
3. Pour in water and knead into dough. Refrigerate for 30 minutes.
4. Roll it out to 3 mm thick. Cut into 4 x 3 inch rectangles. Brush egg yolk over it. Bake at 210°C until golden brown.
5. Pipe mango custard into the pie pastry. Garnish with mango and pomegranate.

Mango Custard

1. Stir egg yolks and sugar together. Heat milk up to 80°C. Add milk to the egg yolk mixture. Stir well.
2. Fold in superfine flour and cornflour. Cook together until thick. Remove from heat.
3. Add mango puree and butter and stir well. Leave it to cool.

派皮

1. 用水拌溶糖和鹽。
2. 篩勻麵粉，加入白油，將白油切成花生般大小。
3. 加入水，用手壓成麵糰，將麵糰冷藏 30 分鐘。
4. 然後將麵糰擀薄至 3 毫米厚，再切成 4 吋 × 3 吋長形，掃蛋黃，以 210℃ 烘焙至金黃色即可。
5. 在烤熟的派皮中間擠上芒果蛋黃醬，用芒果和石榴子裝飾即成。

芒果蛋黃醬

1. 蛋黃加糖攪拌均勻；牛奶加熱至 80℃，加入蛋黃內拌勻。
2. 加入低筋麵粉和粟粉拌勻，一起煮至濃稠，離火。
3. 加入芒果泥和牛油拌勻，待涼備用。

Pine Nut Tarts
松子塔

Tart Pastry
200 g flour
40 g icing sugar
1/4 tsp salt
80 g butter
10 g milk powder
1 egg
1/2 tsp vanilla essence
Filling
150 g pine nuts
50 g syrup
1 tbsp black sesames

塔皮
麵粉 200 克
糖粉 40 克
鹽 1/4 茶匙
牛油 80 克
奶粉 10 克
蛋 1 個
雲尼拿香精 1/2 茶匙
餡料
松子 150 克
糖漿 50 克
黑芝麻 1 湯匙

Method 做法

1. Cream butter until soft. Add sifted icing sugar and salt. Beat until fluffy.
2. Add egg and vanilla essence. Stir well.
3. Sift flour and milk powder onto the worktop. Add butter. Knead into soft dough. Set aside for 30 minutes.
4. Press a small piece of pastry into each greased tart tin. Trim the edges with a spatula. Bake at 180°C for 10 minutes.
5. Mix pine nuts, black sesames and syrup. Place fillings into baked tart crust. Bake at 180°C for further 10 minutes or until golden brown. Serve.

1. 牛油打軟,加入已篩糖粉和鹽,再一起打發。
2. 加入蛋和雲尼拿香精,繼續攪拌均勻。
3. 將麵粉和奶粉篩在工作枱上,倒入已打發的牛油,用手將麵糰壓成軟麵糰,讓麵糰鬆弛 30 分鐘。
4. 取一小塊麵糰壓入已塗油的塔模內,用刮刀去掉多餘的麵糰,以 180℃ 烘烤 10 分鐘。
5. 將松子、黑芝麻和糖漿拌勻,倒進已烤熟的塔皮內,以 180℃ 再烤 10 分鐘至金黃色即可。

Durian Chocolate Puffs
榴槤朱古力泡芙

Cream Puff
130 g butter
250 ml water
1/2 tsp salt
200 g high gluten flour
350 g or 6 eggs
Garnish
50 g nibbed almond
150 g cooking chocolate
Filling
300 g durian puree
50 g whipped cream

泡芙
牛油 130 克
水 250 毫升
鹽 1/2 茶匙
高筋麵粉 200 克
蛋 350 克 /6 個
裝飾
杏仁粒 50 克
煮食朱古力 150 克
餡料
榴槤果肉 300 克
已打發鮮忌廉 50 克

Method 做法

1. Bring butter, salt and water to the boil together over high heat. Pour in high gluten flour. Reduce to low heat. Whisk until smooth (as shown in 1). Remove from heat.
2. Put the smooth dough into the electric mixer and beat until it cools down to lukewarm. Add one egg at a time. Beat for a few minutes or until the mixture is smooth (as shown in 2).
3. Put the mixture in a piping bag. Pipe small balls onto the baking tray. Sprinkle nibbed almond over the balls. Bake at 200°C for 20-25 minutes or until puffs are golden brown. Remove from heat.
4. Finely chop chocolate. Melt in a bowl over simmering water. Dip puffs into melted chocolate.
5. Stir durian puree and whipping cream together. Pipe the durian mixture into the puffs. Serve.

Remark
You must beat the smooth dough and let it cool before adding one egg at a time. Otherwise, the eggs will be cooked.

1. 將牛油、鹽和水一起用大火煮滾，加入高筋麵粉，將火調小，用打蛋器將麵糰攪拌至光滑（看圖 1），離火。
2. 將麵糰放入攪拌機內，攪至溫熱，蛋分多次加入，用攪拌機攪至麵糊光滑（看圖 2）。
3. 將麵糊放進擠花袋內擠出小圓球，表面撒杏仁粒。以 200℃烘焙 20-25 分鐘，至泡芙完全金黃色才取出。
4. 將朱古力切小塊，隔水溶化。泡芙表面蘸朱古力。
5. 榴槤果肉和鮮忌廉一起攪拌，擠進泡芙內即成。

備註
要待麵糰攪拌至微暖才分次加蛋，否則會變成熟蛋。

German Cheese Tarts
德國芝士塔

Tart Pastry
200 g superfine flour
40 g icing sugar
15 g milk powder
10 g grated parmesan
120 g butter
30 g egg

Filling
10 g milk powder
25 g cornflour
60 g sugar
60 g egg yolks
200 ml milk
200 g cream cheese
1 tbsp lemon juice

塔皮
低筋麵粉 200 克
糖粉 40 克
奶粉 15 克
芝士粉 10 克
牛油 120 克
蛋 30 克

餡料
奶粉 10 克
粟粉 25 克
糖 60 克
蛋黃 60 克
牛奶 200 毫升
忌廉芝士 200 克
檸檬汁 1 湯匙

Tart Pastry

1. Sift superfine flour, icing sugar, milk powder and cheese. Add egg and butter. Stir into dough.

2. Set aside for 30 minutes. Press the dough into the tart tin.

3. Bake at 180°C for 10-15 minutes or until tart crust is halfway done.

Filling

1. Stir milk powder, cornflour, 30 g sugar and egg yolks together until well combined. Pour in milk and mix well. Cook over low heat until thick.

2. Blend cream cheese and 30 g sugar until lump-free. Stir in the egg mixture from step (1) gradually. Add lemon juice and combine.

3. Pour the filling into tart pastry. Bake at 150-160°C for 20-25 minutes.

塔皮

1. 將低筋麵粉、糖粉、奶粉和芝士粉一起篩勻，加入蛋和牛油搓成麵糰即可。

2. 讓麵糰鬆弛 30 分鐘，然後將麵糰壓入塔模內。

3. 以 180℃ 烘焙 10-15 分鐘至塔皮半熟即可。

餡料

1. 將奶粉、粟粉、30 克糖和蛋黃一起攪拌至完全調勻，加入牛奶拌勻，用小火煮成濃稠的布丁糊。

2. 忌廉芝士加 30 克糖一起攪拌至沒有顆粒，慢慢加入布丁糊內，拌勻，下檸檬汁，拌勻。

3. 將餡料倒入已烤的塔模內，以150-160℃ 烘焙 20-25 分鐘即成。

Apple Strudel
蘋果酥餅

Pastry
120 g high gluten flour
30 g superfine flour
20 g oil
1 egg yolk
1/4 tsp salt
90 ml warm water

Filling
4 granny smith apples
1 tbsp ground cinnamon
1 tbsp sugar
30 g breadcrumbs
50 g raisins
1 tsp lemon zest
30 g toasted almond flakes

酥皮
高筋麵粉 120 克
低筋麵粉 30 克
油 20 克
蛋黃 1 個
鹽 1/4 茶匙
溫水 90 毫升

餡料
青蘋果 4 個
肉桂粉 1 湯匙
糖 1 湯匙
麵包糠 30 克
葡萄乾 50 克
檸檬皮茸 1 茶匙
烤香杏仁片 30 克

Method | 做法

Filling

1. Peel, core and cut apples into small pieces.
2. Mix all the ingredients and set aside.

Pastry

1. Combine high gluten flour, superfine flour, egg yolk, salt, oil and water. Work into dough. Divide into three portions. Brush oil on the surface. Set aside for at least 1 hour.
2. Sprinkle flour on the dough. Place the dough on a piece of cloth. Roll it out into a 10-inch circle. Stretch the pastry with hands until thin and transparent (as shown in 1-2).
3. Brush melted butter on the surface. Spoon apple fillings along one long edge of the pastry. Fold the pastry to cover the filling (as shown in 3-4). Using the cloth as a guide, roll up from the bottom into a elongated shape (as shown in 5-6).
4. Bake at 200°C for 25 minutes. Serve.

餡料

1. 蘋果去皮、去籽,切小塊。
2. 將所有材料一起拌勻待用。

酥皮

1. 將麵粉、蛋黃、鹽、油和水拌成麵糰,分成3份。麵糰表面塗油,然後讓麵糰鬆弛最少1小時。
2. 在布上灑粉,將麵糰擀開成 10 吋圓麵皮,再用手將麵糰撐開至麵糰成透明的薄麵皮(看圖 1-2)。
3. 在麵糰表面掃上溶化牛油,再將蘋果餡舀在一端,覆上麵皮(看圖 3-4),一邊拉起布、一邊捲麵皮成長條形(看圖 5-6)。
4. 以 200℃烘焙 25 分鐘即可。

TEA • COFFEE

茶 • 咖啡

Tea is the classic companion
to pastries and cakes.
But coffee lovers would have
other obvious choices.
No matter you like coffee or tea,
one of these iced or hot drinks
would fit your taste perfectly.

有美味的甜品豈可沒有飲品配合?
不管你喜歡咖啡或茶,各式冷熱飲品,
總有一款合你心意,
讓我們齊來舉杯吧!

Cinnamon Apple Tea
蘋果肉桂茶

2 apples
4 sticks cinnamon
1 litre water
蘋果 2 粒
肉桂條 4 條
水 1 公升

Method 做法

1. Cut each apple into 8 pieces.
2. Bring water, apple and cinnamon sticks to the boil over high heat. Cook for 20 minutes and serve.

1. 蘋果切成 8 塊。
2. 蘋果、水和肉桂條一起用大火煮 20 分鐘，即可享用。

it's tea time!

Jasmine Iced Coffee
茉莉茶冰咖啡

Ingredients 材料

1 tbsp honey
crushed ice
1/2 cup iced coffee
1/2 cup jasmine
green tea
蜂蜜 1 湯匙
碎冰適量
冰咖啡 1/2 杯
茉莉綠茶 1/2 杯

Method 做法

1. Add honey, crushed ice, iced coffee and jasmine green tea in this order.
2. Mix well. Serve.

1. 杯中依序加入蜂蜜、碎冰、冰咖啡和茉莉綠茶。
2. 拌勻即可享用。

Rose and Rosemary Tea

玫瑰迷迭香茶

Ingredients 材料

5-6 stalks rosemary
20 dried roses
sugar
500 ml hot water
迷迭香 5-6 根
乾燥玫瑰 20 朵
糖隨意
熱水 500 毫升

Method 做法

1. Warm the teapot and teacups.
2. Put dried roses, rosemary and sugar into the teapot. Pour in water of 80°C. Cover for a while and transfer to cups. Serve.

1. 先將茶壺和杯子加熱。
2. 將玫瑰、迷迭香和糖放入茶壺內，沖入 80℃熱水，稍微悶一會兒，即可倒入杯中飲用。

This tea removes fat and whets the appetite.

＊這茶有消脂、開胃的作用。

Lemongrass Mint Tea
薄荷香茅提神茶

Ingredients 材料

20-30 peppermint leaves
2 stalks lemongrass
500 ml hot water
薄荷葉 20-30 片，香茅 2
枝，熱水 500 毫升

Method 做法

1. Warm the teapot and teacups.
2. Put mint leaves and lemongrass into the teapot. Pour in water of 80°C. Cover the lid for a while. Pour tea into cup and serve.

1. 將茶壺和杯子加熱。
2. 將薄荷葉和香茅放入茶壺內，沖入大約 80℃ 的熱水，稍微悶一會兒，即可倒入杯中飲用。

This tea is refreshing and helps digestion.

　　這茶可提神、助消化。

let's have a break!

作者：
許曉翠

編輯：
譚麗琴

美術設計：
羅美齡

攝影：
Continental
Element SDN BHD

出版者：
海濱圖書公司
大眾控股集團成員
荃灣德士古道 220-248 號荃灣工業中心 14 樓
電話：852-2408 8801　傳真： 852-2408 2306
印刷者：
復興橡皮印刷有限公司
荃灣德士古道 220-248 號荃灣工業中心 14 樓
電話：852-2408 8801　傳真： 852-2408 2306
總代理：世界出版社
荃灣德士古道 220-248 號荃灣工業中心 14 樓
電話：852-2408 8801　傳真： 852-2408 2306
大眾書局門市部：
九龍黃埔花園十一期聚寶坊地庫 B1b 號舖
九龍旺角新世紀廣場668，686-687號舖
九龍樂富商場第一期F10至F11號舖
九龍藍田康田苑啟田道35號地下
九龍將軍澳尚德商場202號舖
九龍黃大仙中心商場地庫B16號舖
新界沙田新城市廣場第一期四樓445-447號舖
新界大埔超級城B區2樓270-272號舖
新加坡總代理：
諾文文化事業私人有限公司
NOVUM ORGANUM PUBLISHING HOUSE (PTE) LTD.
20 Old Toh Tuck Road
Singapore 597655
Tel: 65-6462 6141　Fax: 65-6469 4043
馬來西亞總代理：
諾文文化事業有限公司
NOVUM ORGANUM PUBLISHING HOUSE (MALAYSIA) SDN BHD.
No. 8, Jalan 7/118B, Desa Tun Razak,
56000 Kuala Lumpur, Malaysia
Tel: 603-9179 6333　Fax: 603-9179 6200
台灣總代理：
大眾雨晨圖書有限公司
台北縣中和市中正路872號10樓
電話: 02-3234 7887　傳真: 02-3234 3931
電郵: ycbook@popularworld.com
24hrs語音補書專線：02-3234 8833
出版日期：2006年5月

ISBN-13:978-988-202-351-2
ISBN-10:988-202-351-7
PUBLISHED IN HONG KONG